The Krampus Night Before Christmas

'TWAS – The Krampus Night Before Christmas is unlike other books. In fact, it is a portal to a magical wintry world, and an adventure inspired by the literature and legends of Christmas.

As well as the book itself, you will need two dice (or a standard pack of playing cards), a pencil and an eraser. Using these tools, and a simple set of game rules contained within the book, you will undertake an epic quest to rescue Father Christmas from the anti-Santa Krampus, and avert a Christmas catastrophe.

YOU decide which route to take, which risks to brave, and even which of the strange creatures you will meet along the way to engage in battle. But be warned – whether you succeed in your quest, or meet a dire end, will be down to the choices YOU make.

Will you be able to save Santa?

Proudly Published by Snowbooks in 2019

Snowbooks Ltd.
email: info@snowbooks.com
www.snowbooks.com

British Library Cataloguing in Publication Data
A catalogue record for this book is available from the British Library.

Hardcover 978-1-911390-69-5
Paperback 978-1-911390-70-1
Ebook 978-1-911390-68-8

With thanks to the Krampusnacht Play-Testers:

James A Hirons, Jason Vince a.k.a. Dreamwalker Spirit, Sterling R. Scherff, Vitas Varnas, Steve Pitson, Fabrice Gatille, Crystal McCarty, Andreas Brückner, David Poppel, Andrés Rodríguez Rodríguez, DK, 林立人 Lin Liren, René Batsford, Kevin Abbotts, Colin Deady, Colin Oaten, Harvey Howell, Judykins, Simon J. Painter, Stephanie M., Javier Fernández-Sanguino, Sauro Lepri, Simon Scott, Drew Smith, Allan Matthews, Arthur Lewis Settle, Kristen Patton-Schulle, Betsy J, Timithy Klesick, Rob Lord, Naked Genius, Bryan K. Borgman, Jonathan Caines, Rhel, Ondřej Zástěra, Alexander Ballingall

With special thanks to Paul Simpson

The Krampus Night Before Christmas

Written by JONATHAN GREEN

Illustrated By TONY HOUGH

SNOWBOOKS

Also by Jonathan Green

ACE Gamebooks
Alice's Nightmare in Wonderland
The Wicked Wizard of Oz
NEVERLAND – Here Be Monsters!
Beowulf Beastslayer

Snowbooks Fantasy Histories
You Are The Hero – A History of Fighting Fantasy Gamebooks
You Are The Hero Part 2

Snowbooks Anthologies
Sharkpunk (edited by Jonathan Green)
Game Over (edited by Jonathan Green)
Shakespeare Vs Cthulhu (edited by Jonathan Green)

Fighting Fantasy Gamebooks
Spellbreaker
Knights of Doom
Curse of the Mummy
Bloodbones
Howl of the Werewolf
Stormslayer
Night of the Necromancer

Sonic the Hedgehog Adventure Gamebooks
Theme Park Panic (with Marc Gascoigne)
Stormin' Sonic (with Marc Gascoigne)

Doctor Who Adventure Gamebooks
Decide Your Destiny: The Horror of Howling Hill
Choose The Future: Night of the Kraken

Star Wars: The Clone Wars – Decide Your Destiny
Crisis on Coruscant

Gamebook Adventures
Temple of the Spider God

Warlock's Bounty
Revenge of the Sorcerer

Path to Victory
Herald of Oblivion
Shadows Over Sylvania

’Twas the Dedication Before Christmas

After Clement Clarke Moore

’Twas the night before Christmas, when all through the house
Not a creature was stirring, not even a mouse.
The stockings were hung by the chimney with care,
In hopes that St. Nicholas soon would be there.
Hattie and Dylan were snug in their beds,
While visions of chocolate cake danced in their heads.
But on hearing a thud, and hearing a clatter,
The boy went downstairs to see what was the matter.
On ent’ring the parlour he gave a great laugh,
To see someone large sitting there by the hearth,
For the caller in red was all filthy and black,
From the beard on his face to the sack on his back.
“Who are you?” asked the boy. There was soot on the floor.
“Did you come down the chimney? What’s wrong with the door?”
“’Twas locked,” said the old man. “So please don’t object.
Besides, it’s tradition – what people expect.”
Reaching into his bag he said, “I must be swift,
But I’ve called in this evening to give you this gift.”
The parcel was small and wrapped in brown paper.
“For me?” laughed the boy. “This is a strange caper!”
“A present for you,” said the saint, “take a look.”
The boy ripped it open and gasped, “It’s a book!”
St. Nicholas smiled, his face wrinkled with age.
“Look inside,” he said, “quick, at this one special page.”
The lad opened the tome and began to flick through it.
“It’s a game,” said Saint Nick. “You’ll have fun if you do it.”
And right at the front, the book’s author had written,
“For Alex, my nephew, with whom we’re all smitten.”

The Krampus Night Before Christmas

In the Deep Midwinter

Introduction

The book you hold in your hands is the gateway to a magical wintery world, and an adventure inspired by the literature and legends of Christmas. Once inside its pages, you will undertake an epic quest to rescue Father Christmas from the anti-Santa Krampus, and avert a festive apocalypse.

For this is no ordinary book. Rather than reading it from cover to cover, you will discover that at the end of each narrative section you will be presented with a series of choices that allow you to control the course of the story.

In *'TWAS – The Krampus Night Before Christmas* you become the hero of the adventure, directing the course of the narrative thanks to the choices you make, as you undertake an epic quest. Success is by no means certain and you may well fail to complete the adventure at your first attempt. However, with experience, skill, and maybe even a little luck, each new attempt should bring you closer to your ultimate goal.

In addition to the book itself, you will need two six-sided dice, or a conventional pack of 52 playing cards, a pencil, an eraser, and a copy of the *'TWAS – The Krampus Night Before Christmas* Adventure Sheet (spare copies of which can be downloaded from www.acegamebooks.com).

Playing the Game

There are three ways to play through *'TWAS – The Krampus Night Before Christmas*. The first is to use two conventional six-sided dice. The second is to use a conventional pack of 52 playing cards. The third is to ignore the rules altogether and just read the book, making choices as appropriate, but ignoring any combat or attribute tests, always assuming you win every battle and pass every skill test. (Even if you play the adventure this way, there is still no guarantee that you will complete it at your first attempt.)

If you are opting to play through *'TWAS – The Krampus Night Before Christmas* using the game rules, you first need to determine your strengths and weaknesses.

Your Attributes

You have three attributes you will need to keep track of during the course of the adventure, using the Adventure Sheet. Some of these will change frequently, others less so, but it is important that you keep an accurate record of the current level for all of them.

Agility – This is a measure of how athletic and agile you are. If you need to leap across a chasm or dodge a deadly projectile, this is the attribute that will be employed.

Combat – This is a measure of how skilful you are at fighting, whether it be in unarmed combat, or wielding a keen-edged blade in battle.

Endurance – This is a measure of how physically tough you are and how much strength you have left. This attribute will vary more than any other during the course of your adventure.

Unlike some adventure gamebooks, in *'TWAS – The Krampus Night Before Christmas* your strengths and weaknesses are not determined randomly. Instead, you get to decide what you are good at and, conversely, what you might not be so good at.

Your *Agility* and *Combat* attributes start at a base level of 6. Your *Endurance* score starts at a base level of 20. You then have a pool of 10 extra points to share out between *Agility*, *Combat* and *Endurance* as you see fit, but you can only add up to 5 points to each attribute. So the maximum starting score for

Agility and *Combat* is 11, and the maximum starting score for *Endurance* is 25. (You must apportion all 10 points one way or another, and cannot leave any unused.)

For example, you might choose to add nothing to your *Agility* score, 5 points to your *Combat* score, and add the remaining 5 points to your *Endurance* score, making you a mighty warrior and giving you the following starting profile for the game:

Agility = 6, *Combat* = 11, *Endurance* = 25.

Alternatively, you might want to add 4 points to your *Agility* and *Combat* scores, and the remaining 2 points to your *Endurance* score, making you more of an all-rounder, and giving you this starting profile:

Agility = 10, *Combat* = 10, *Endurance* = 22.

Having determined where your strengths and weaknesses lie, record the value of each attribute in the appropriate box on the Adventure Sheet in pencil, and make sure you have an eraser to hand, as they will doubtless all change at some point as you play through the adventure (and some more than others).

There are limits on how high each of your attributes can be at the start of the adventure, but there are also limits on how high they can be raised during the course of the adventure, dependent upon bonus points you may be awarded. Neither your *Agility* score nor your *Combat* score may exceed 12 points, while your *Endurance* score may not exceed 30 points. However, should your *Endurance* score ever drop to zero, or below, then your adventure is over and you should stop reading immediately; if you want to tackle the quest again, you will have to start from the beginning, determining your attributes anew, and then starting the story from section 1 once more.

Testing Your Attributes

At various times during the adventure, you will be asked to test one or more of your attributes.

If it is your *Agility* or *Combat* that is being tested, simply roll two dice. If the total rolled is equal to or less than the particular attribute being tested, you have passed the test; if the total rolled is greater than the attribute in question, then you have failed the test. (If you are using playing cards, draw one card; picture cards are worth 11 and an Ace is worth 12.)

If it is your *Endurance* score that is being tested, roll four dice in total. If the combined score of all four dice is equal to or less than your *Endurance* score, then you have passed the test, but if it is greater, then what is being asked of you is beyond what you are capable of and you have failed the test. (If you are using playing cards, draw two cards and add their values together; picture cards are worth 11 and an Ace is worth 12.)

Restoring Your Attributes

There are various ways that you can restore lost attribute points, or be granted bonuses that take your attributes beyond their starting scores, and these will be described in the text.

However, an easy way to restore lost *Endurance* points is to find sustenance. Sometimes you may find enough food that you can take some with you to consume later on in the adventure.

Make sure that if you do find any supplies of this nature you record them on your Adventure Sheet, along with any information about exactly how many attribute points they will restore when consumed. (Unless you are told otherwise by the text, one Meal will restore 4 *Endurance points.)*

Special Abilities

In addition to your three basic attributes, you also have two special abilities that you can employ at critical moments during your journey through the nightmarish winter wonderland you are about to enter:

Naughty or Nice – If you find yourself in a tight spot, you can use this ability to change the nature of the magical world around you. However, this may result in you actually making things worse for yourself, rather than better.

The Pen is Mightier – This ability allows you to avoid coming to blows with an enemy, by altering the narrative of the encounter and thereby enabling you to get away unscathed.

These very special abilities can only be used three times each during the course of the adventure. Each time you call on one of them, you must cross off a box on your Adventure Sheet under the appropriate special ability.

Combat

You will repeatedly be called upon to defend yourself against the denizens of the warped winter wonderland. Sometimes you may even choose to attack these horrors yourself. After all, as they say, the best form of defence is attack.

When this happens, start by filling in your opponent's *Combat* and *Endurance* scores in the first available 'TWAS Encounter Box on your Adventure Sheet.

Whenever you engage in combat, you will be told in the text whether you or your enemy has the initiative; in other words, who has the advantage and gets to attack first.

1. Roll two dice and add your *Combat* score. The resulting total is your *Combat Rating*.
2. Roll two dice and add your opponent's *Combat* score. The resulting total is your opponent's *Combat Rating*.
3. In each Combat Round, add a temporary 1 point bonus to the *Combat Rating* of whichever of the combatants has the initiative for the duration of that round only.
4. If your *Combat Rating* is higher than your opponent's you have wounded your enemy; deduct 2 points from your opponent's *Endurance* score, and move on to step 7.

5. If your opponent's *Combat Rating* is higher, then you have been wounded; deduct 2 points from your *Endurance* score, and move on to step 8.
6. If your *Combat Rating* and your opponent's *Combat Rating* are the same, roll one die. If the number rolled is odd, you and your opponent deflect each other's attacks; go to step 10. If the number rolled is even, go to step 9.
7. If your opponent's *Endurance* score has been reduced to zero or below, you have won; the battle is over and you can continue on your way. If your opponent is not yet dead, go to step 10.
8. If your *Endurance* score has been reduced to zero or below, your opponent has won the battle. If you want to continue your adventure you will have to start again from the beginning, determining your strengths and weaknesses anew. However, if you are still alive, go to step 10.
9. You and your opponent have both managed to injure each other; deduct 1 point from both your *Endurance* score and your opponent's *Endurance* score. If your *Endurance* score has been reduced to zero or below, your adventure is over; if you want to play again you will have to start again from the beginning. If you are still alive but your enemy's *Endurance* has been reduced to zero or below, you have won; the battle is over and you can continue on your way. If neither you nor your opponent are dead, go to step 10.
10. If you won the Combat Round, you will have the initiative in the next Combat Round. If your opponent won the Combat Round, they will have the initiative. If neither of you won the Combat Round, neither of you will gain the initiative bonus for the next Combat Round. Go back to step 1 and work through the sequence again until either your opponent is dead, or you are defeated.

Occasionally you may find yourself having to fight more than one opponent at once. Such concurrent battles are conducted in the same way as above, using the ten-step process, except that you will have to work out the *Combat Ratings* of all those involved. As long as you have a higher rating than an opponent you will injure them, no matter how many opponents you are taking on at the same time. However, equally, any opponent with a *Combat Rating* higher than yours will be able to injure you too.

An Alternative to Dice

Rather than rolling dice, you may prefer to determine random numbers during the game using a pack of playing cards.

To do this, when you are called upon to roll dice, simply shuffle a standard 52-card deck (having removed the jokers) and draw a single card. (If you are asked to roll four dice, draw two cards.) Number cards are worth the number shown on the card. Jacks, Queens and Kings are all worth 11, and if you draw an Ace, it counts as being worth 12 (for example, if you are engaged in combat), and is an automatic pass if you are testing an attribute – any attribute.

After drawing from the deck you can either return any cards you have drawn or, using the Pontoon method, leave those drawn cards out of the deck. Both styles of play will influence how lucky, or unlucky, you may be during the game, when it comes to determining random numbers.

Equipment

You start your adventure with nothing but the pyjamas you are wearing, a dressing-gown, bed socks, and a pair of slippers. During the course of your quest you will no doubt acquire all manner of other items that may be of use to you later on. Anything that you do collect should be recorded on your Adventure Sheet, including any clues or passwords, as well as weapons, provisions, and other miscellaneous objects.

Any items that provide bonuses for your attributes, such as a magic sword that adds 1 point to your *Combat* score in battle, only provide those bonuses when the item in question is in use. Just because you own a magic sword does not mean that your *Combat* score is automatically 1 point higher.

Hints on Play

There is more than one path that you can follow through *'TWAS – The Krampus Night Before Christmas* to reach your ultimate goal, but it may take you several attempts to actually complete the adventure. Make notes and draw a map as you explore. This map will doubtless prove invaluable during future attempts at completing the quest, and will allow you to progress more speedily in order to reach unexplored regions.

Keep a careful eye on all of your attributes throughout the game. Beware of traps and setting off on wild goose chases. However, it would be wise to collect useful items along the way that may aid you further on in your quest.

Ending the Game

There are several ways that your adventure can end. If your *Endurance* score ever drops to zero or below, your trials have exhausted and overcome you. If this happens, stop reading at once.

There may also be occasions where you are prevented from progressing any further through the adventure thanks to the choices you have made, or if you meet a sudden and untimely end. In all of these cases, if you want to have another crack at completing the adventure you will have to start again with a new Adventure Sheet and begin the story afresh from the beginning.

There is, of course, one other reason for your adventure coming to an end, and that is if you successfully complete your quest, the very same quest that awaits you now...

The Krampus Night Before Christmas
Adventure Sheet

AGILITY	SPECIAL ABILITIES
	THE PEN IS MIGHTIER
COMBAT	NAUGHTY OR NICE
ENDURANCE	MEALS
EQUIPMENT	CODEWORDS

THE PEN IS MIGHTIER

NAUGHTY OR NICE

Encounter Boxes

AGILITY =
ENDURANCE =

AGILITY =
ENDURANCE =

AGILITY =
ENDURANCE =

AGILITY =
ENDURANCE =

AGILITY =
ENDURANCE =

AGILITY =
ENDURANCE =

AGILITY =
ENDURANCE =

AGILITY =
ENDURANCE =

AGILITY =
ENDURANCE =

AGILITY =
ENDURANCE =

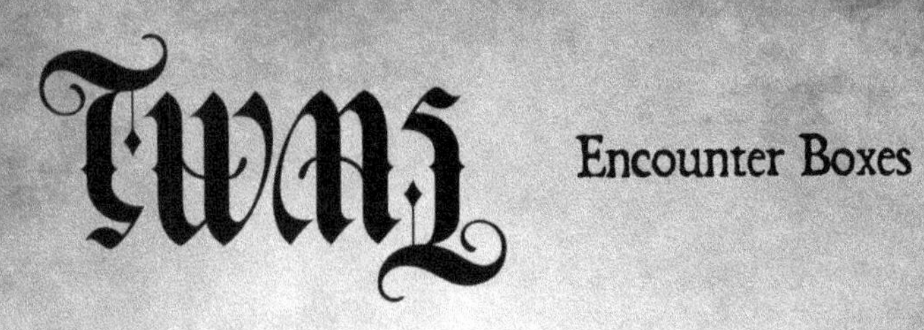

Encounter Boxes

AGILITY =
ENDURANCE =

AGILITY =
ENDURANCE =

AGILITY =
ENDURANCE =

AGILITY =
ENDURANCE =

AGILITY =
ENDURANCE =

AGILITY =
ENDURANCE =

AGILITY =
ENDURANCE =

AGILITY =
ENDURANCE =

AGILITY =
ENDURANCE =

AGILITY =
ENDURANCE =

’Twas the Night Before Christmas...

When all through the house
Not a creature was stirring, not even a mouse;
The stockings were hung by the chimney with care,
In hopes that St. Nicholas soon would be there;
The children were nestled all snug in their beds,
While visions of sugarplums danced in their heads.

You wake with a start, as the clock in the hall starts to chime. You lie there listening – the bedcovers pulled up tight under your chin, your heart beating an excited tattoo, like a little drummer boy – wondering if He’s been yet. It is Christmas Eve after all.

Eleven...

Twelve...

Thirteen.

The crystal clear ringing of the last chime echoes through the silent house.

Thirteen chimes? There must be something wrong with the clock.

You are just wondering whether you should go and take a look when you hear a crash come from somewhere downstairs, followed by a heavy thud. You stay where you are, your body fizzing with adrenalin, wondering what could have made the noise – are you being burgled? – and whether someone else is going to investigate.

But after several long seconds have passed, without hearing any of the other bedroom doors open, your curiosity can take it no longer, and you decide to take a look for yourself.

Getting out of bed, you pull on your dressing gown, over your pyjamas, put on your slippers, and quietly creep out of your room.

The full moon is visible through the window at the end of the landing – someone having forgotten to draw the curtains upon going to bed – and so, by its wan light, with silent footsteps you cautiously make your way downstairs.

Now turn to **1**.

1

At the bottom of the stairs stands the old grandfather clock that just chimed thirteen. Sprigs of holly and garlands of tinsel adorn it and the rest of the furniture in the hallway.

The front door to the house is before you and remains closed, and there is no sign of anyone having entered this way. To your right is the door to the sitting room, while to your left is the door to the dining room.

Do you want to:

Examine the grandfather clock? Turn to **78**.

Open the front door? Turn to **15**.

Open the door to the sitting room? Turn to **159**.

Open the door to the dining room? Turn to **141**.

2

Locking someone up in a cage until you're ready to butcher them and pop them in a cauldron of boiling water isn't what you would consider a good example of Christmas cheer. Where's the trolls' festive spirit? Whatever happened to 'goodwill to all men'? Do they know it's Christmas?

"Please don't eat me," you plead with your captors. "I'm sorry I strayed into your territory. Please let me out; it is Christmas after all!"

Roll one die (or pick a card). If the number rolled is odd (or the card is red), turn to **138**. If the number rolled is even (or the card is black), turn to **118**.

3

The box starts to jerk and twitch, as if with a life of its own. Answering its insistent call to be taken out, the moment you do so, the lid of the box springs open and out pours a torrent of glowing, ethereal forms.

The spirits captured by the box rise into the sky where they assail the ragged things circling there, which give voice to banshee wails of alarm and distress.

Turn to **383**.

4

The door is opened by a burly man, with muscular arms and a thick black beard. He is wearing a sturdy leather apron, and what clothes of his that are visible, along with his hands and face, are black with soot. Catching sight of the ruddy glow coming from the forge at the back of the hovel, you realise he must be a blacksmith.

When he sees you standing there, he looks you up and down in surprise, his gaze lingering on your slippered feet. Then, as if suddenly remembering himself, he ushers you inside and shuts the door.

"You look like you're about to catch your death," he says. "Come, warm yourself by the fire."

If you have the code word *Kold* recorded on your Adventure Sheet, turn to **22**. If not, turn to **42.**

5

As you enter the kitchen, you feel a cold gust of air and then the back door slams shut. Some*thing*, or some*one*, was just in here. Your pulse starts to quicken once more.

Will you open the back door, in the hope of catching whoever was just in here (turn to **342**), search the kitchen for clues as to who might have been here (turn to **302**), or run back upstairs to bed and hide under the covers (turn to **98**)?

6

The flock of imps suddenly flies away, heading north, towards the mountains… or so it seems.

In that moment of distraction you do not realise that one of the horrors has remained behind, until it descends and grabs you by the shoulders, pulling you from the back of the broomstick.

As La Befana is about to give chase, the flock of devils returns to torment her, their diabolical ruse having worked, and stop her from coming to your aid. As the imp carrying you flies away northwards, over the wintry wilderness, you fight to free yourself from its clutches.

Take a Combat test; if you pass the test, turn to **26**, but if you fail the test, turn to **46**.

7

Suddenly beset by a grinding of gears, you look up to discover that you are locked within the targeting sights of a mechanical toy robot. It is taller than you are, and its eye-visor glows with a malevolent red light, while bolts of blue lighting arc between the antennae protruding from its angular head.

As it raises its arms, you see that in its hands the robot is holding a pair of glowing ray guns, in the split-second before it unleashes a fusillade of coruscating energy-beams.

If you are in possession of the Box of Delights, turn to **212**. If not, turn to **173**.

8

You gobble up some peppermint creams, whilst loading your pockets with marzipan fruits and sugared almonds. (Gain 1 *Endurance* point and add 2 Meals to your Adventure Sheet.)

However, as you are busy stuffing your face with confections and snaffling sweetmeats, you do not realise that the nutcracker standing on the sideboard – carved and painted to resemble a soldier – is jerkily coming to life, until suddenly it is there in front of you, trying to strike you with the rod attached to its left arm.

If you want to call on your *The Pen is Mightier* special ability, turn to **58**. If not, turn to **28**.

9

Hearing an unexpected throaty bellow of a roar, you turn in abject terror and surprise to see a huge white-furred monster bounding towards you. The polar bear moves with great lolloping strides, its claws finding purchase on the frost-rimed flagstones, and the flesh of its black maw flapping as it runs.

But the savage arctic predator isn't here for you – it's come for the ice witch!

Charging past you, it rears up on its hind-legs, bringing its lethal claws to bear against the sorceress. And then the two are lost from sight as the Snow Queen's conjured blizzard returns and carries the two combatants away.

Cross off one use of *The Pen is Mightier* special ability and turn to **227**.

10

"Come in out of the cold," you tell the shivering young woman, when you suddenly notice that, under her skirts, rather than feet she has the cloven hooves of a goat.

Immediately, you try to slam the door shut again, but the deceiving demon is already half over the threshold. Trapped there, she undergoes a hideous transformation; her fingernails become savage claws, while her beautiful visage gives way to a twisted demonic leer.

If you want to use *The Pen is Mightier* special ability, cross off one use and turn to **180**. If not, turn to **60**.

11

With a snapping of wood and shearing of metal, the sleigh slams into the ground, and you and the sinister creature are violently thrown out by the force of the impact.

If you want to invoke your *Naughty or Nice* special ability now, and you still can, cross off one use and turn to **175**. If not, turn to **155**.

12

Taking a firm hold of the white-wood spear, you take aim and hurl it through the cold night air, straight at the goat-leggéd freak.

Take a Combat test. If you pass the test, turn to **94**. If you fail the test, turn to **257**.

13

As the sleigh moves towards the edge of the roof, its runners bumping over the tiles, you start to run. Your slippers threatening to take your feet from under you, you nonetheless manage to catch up with the sleigh — just as the reindeer throw themselves into the teeth of the blizzard — and pull yourself up onto the tailboard as the vehicle leaves the roof.

Hauling yourself on board, you slide down among the sacks that fill the huge sleigh, unseen by its sinister driver.

But one of the sacks, which is larger than the rest, is wriggling, as whoever – or whatever! – is inside it, struggles to get out.

If you want to untie the knotted cord that is keeping the sack closed, turn to **144**. If you would rather not risk unleashing what might be lurking within, turn to **113.**

14

"Curse you, stranger!" the wretched Venceslav shouts from behind the still firmly locked cell door. "May your extremities feel the bite of the frost and drop off!"

A chill suddenly shivers through you, even worse than the icy atmosphere of the courtyard.

Cross off one use of *The Pen is Mightier* special ability, and one use of the *Naughty or Nice* special ability, if you have any to lose, and then turn to **381**.

15

The moment you open the door the blizzard hits you! It's blowing a gale outside, one that is rapidly sucking the warmth from the hall as snow is swept inside by the icy wind.

Do you want to quickly slam the door shut again (turn to **35**), or go outside to investigate further (turn to **55**)?

16

"Candyman. Candyman! *Candyman!"* you cry.

It suddenly feels as if the atmosphere in the room has thickened to the consistency of melting toffee. Something is definitely happening, but it isn't what you had intended.

As you watch, the Candyman appears to increase in stature, and as he opens his liquorice mouth in an exultant roar, you can hear a sound like popping candy exploding inside him. By invoking his name, you have managed to boost the powers of the sweet-toothed terror, so you're going to have to cut him down to size again! (In this battle, the Candyman has the initiative.)

CANDYMAN	COMBAT 9	ENDURANCE 11

If you manage to hack the spun-sugar super-being to bits, turn to **430**.

17

You can hear the words of the nursery rhyme in your head as the tinkling tune box plays on:

Half a pound of tuppenny rice,
Half a pound of treacle,
That's the way the money goes,
Pop goes the weasel!

At "Pop!" the Jack-in-the-Box springs open and a demented jester-like character, with an over-large smile splitting its porcelain face, flies out. The jester has stiletto-blades for fingers, and below its waist there is nothing by a shrouded spring.

A horrible, high-pitched giggle, running on repeat, comes from somewhere inside its chest, rather than its insanely leering mouth, as the Jack-in-the-Box lurches for you.

If you want to employ *The Pen is Mightier* special ability, turn to **209**. If not, turn to **101**.

18

You enter a much larger room, dominated by a table that has been laid for Christmas dinner, with place settings for twelve people. There are bowls of crispy roast potatoes, succulent pigs-in-blankets, sprouts by the bucket-load, and, at the centre of the table, a magnificent turkey. The aroma that assails you is the very definition of Christmas!

If you want to sit down at the table and help yourself to some of the food, turn to **103**. If you can resist the tempting smells, you leave the dining room through a door on the far side – turn to **492**.

19

You suspected that it would come to this in the end, and so steal yourself to fight.

If you want to use *The Pen is Mightier* special ability, and you still can, turn to **52**. If not, make a note that you have the initiative and then turn to **203**.

20

Beyond the bells, you set off again along the corridor, hoping that no other obstacles appear to hamper your progress. But you are soon disappointed, when a hatch opens in the floor and a wooden automaton rises from it.

It looks like a dragon. A complicated arrangement of cogs and gears cause its wooden wings to flap and its jaws to open, before snapping shut again, over and over, while its claws flail at you. It is not sentient, merely a machine, but you are still going to have to battle your way past it – unless you have a better idea?

If you wish to use *The Pen is Mightier* special ability now, and you still can, turn to **70**. If not, turn to **140**.

21

It is then that you notice the groove in the floor of the stable, delineating the edge of a trapdoor – a possible means of escape!

As the imps look inside one of the other stalls, you dart out of your hiding place, ease the trapdoor open – thank goodness it wasn't padlocked shut – and slip through it into the darkness below.

Turn to **275**.

22

It is wonderfully warm inside the forge, and the heat is already starting to chase the cold from your bones.

Restore 1 *Combat* point and 1 *Agility* point, and then turn to **42**.

23

The Elves burst from the dungeon cell and charge along the corridor beyond, shouting and hollering, carrying you along with them. From there they rampage through Mrs Christmas's kitchens, and do not stop until they enter Santa's workshop, a place that overwhelms you with its sheer scale and deafening noise.

The heart of Father Christmas's toy factory is one enormous production line. Miles and miles of clanking wooden conveyor belts criss-cross the cyclopean space, which is also decorated with a veritable forest of Christmas trees, which in turn are adorned with miles of tinsel and a profusion of blown-glass baubles. And everywhere you look there are mountains of presents.

At first you take the factory workforce to be Elves as well, until you focus on their hideous features and leering demonic sneers. These aren't Santa's little helpers! They look more like Satan's little helpers!

The toys the horrible impish creatures are manufacturing don't look like the sort of thing you would imagine many children will have written down on their Christmas lists this year. There are grim-face dolls wielding bloody axes, headless teddy bears, and clockwork creations with snapping gin-trap jaws.

Upon seeing the imps and the booby-trapped toys they are making, a roar of rage rises from the Elves and they pour into the workshop. Arming themselves with anything that comes to hand – from spanners and screwdrivers, to mallets and crowbars – the Elves attack the Imps.

As the Elves engage the impish army in pitched battle, pointing towards a wooden staircase at the far end of the hall and the grand set of double doors at the top, the Chief Elf Jingle calls out to you, "Find Father Christmas!"

You don't need to be told twice! You sprint for the stairs, taking them two at a time, and, throw yourself through the doors, entering the centre of operations here at the North Pole.

Turn to **485.**

24

Battling the effects of cold water shock that threaten to send you into a drowning panic, you fight to keep your head above the water until you can get a hand on the ice and somehow manage to claw your way back onto the frozen surface of the river.

However, your freezing dip has taken its toll. (Deduct 2 *Endurance* points, 1 *Combat* point, and 1 *Agility* point.)

Shivering with cold, you struggle to your feet to find that the strange figure that led you to your brush with death has vanished, and so you make your way back to the frost fair.

In the shadow of one of the bridge's stone arches, you see that someone has set up a Punch and Judy show. Standing beside the red-and-yellow-striped canvas booth is a little old man in a worn grey overcoat and wide-brimmed hat, with a thick white beard, and a red spotted kerchief tied about his neck.

The old man's dog, an Irish terrier, runs over to you and starts skipping around your feet.

Turn to **447**.

25

Pulling the belt of your dressing-gown tight and taking a deep breath, you start to climb the fissured face of the glacier, searching for hand-holds and protrusions upon the ice-cliff.

Take an Endurance test. If you pass the test, turn to **45**, but if you fail the test, turn to **65**.

26

You manage to struggle free of the imp's clutches, but instantly drop like a stone towards the ground far below.

Fortunately, you land in a deep snowdrift which breaks your fall. Clambering out of the drift, you set off, alone again, through the deep, dark forest.

Turn to **213**.

27

It's not only curiosity that killed the cat – not anymore.

Leaving the hunter dead in the snow, you set off once again, through the forest.

Turn to **453**.

28

You have no choice but to defend yourself, as best you can, from the Nutcracker's bludgeoning blows and champing, sharp metal teeth. (In this battle, the Nutcracker has the initiative.)

NUTCRACKER	COMBAT 7	ENDURANCE 5

If you defeat the animated nutcracker, turn to **84**.

29

Throwing yourself forwards, you roll across the floor, the robot's fusillade of laser-fire hitting the door — which you were standing in front of until only a moment ago — and come back up onto your feet, right next to the robot.

Knocking the guns from its pincer-claw hands, you prepare to take on the battery-powered brute.

If you want to employ *The Pen is Mightier* special ability, and you still can, turn to **149**. If not, make a note that in the battle to come you have the initiative and turn to **179**.

30

Its giggles giving way to banshee-like wails, the Perchta launches itself at you! (In this battle, your attacker has the initiative.)

PERCHTA	COMBAT 7	ENDURANCE 6

If you beat the possessed puppet, it flops onto the floor in front of the fire – turn to **82**.

31

Beaten back by the devil's brutal blows, as the sleigh lurches suddenly, you lose your balance and find yourself toppling out backwards. And then you're tumbling through the snow-swept sky, dropping like a stone towards the ground.

Turn to **235**.

32

The gingerbread men are just now so many pieces of broken biscuit and piles of crumbs scattered on the floor of the kitchen.

As you are wondering whether your battle with the kitchen's strange guardians has exposed your presence to the goblin cooks, you notice the pieces of gingerbread skittering across the floor towards each other, forming into one great mound, which then starts to swell and grow.

In no time at all the doughy mass is as tall as you are, and limbs extrude from the giant ball of gingerbread as it takes on a recognisably humanoid form once again.

Now turn to **377**.

33

The saucepan hits the hobgoblin, who cries out in pain as he is drenched, from head to toe, in its scalding contents. The cry becomes a shriek, and the shriek a scream, as his icy form immediately begins to melt – ice turning to water, and water turning to steam, as it evaporates.

Soon there is nothing left of your attacker but a puddle of water on the floor.

Turn to **355**.

34

Entering the north-west tower, you are confronted by a door of solid, iron-bound oak, which is firmly locked. However, the sound you make as you try the handle alerts the person imprisoned within to your presence.

A haggard face appears at the small barred window in the door, set amidst the tangle of an unruly grey beard, while a pair of red-rimmed eyes peer out at you. As they focus on you, a wild smile spreads across the face and a cracked voice says, "Stranger, are you here to save me?"

"Who are you?" you ask.

"My name is Venceslav, and this castle once belonged to me – that is until the Snow Queen seized it from me and turned the members of my court into those ice sculptures you must have seen in the courtyard. Let me out and together we can rid ourselves of the usurping ice-witch!"

If you want to release the prisoner, turn to **72**. But how do you know if he's telling the truth? If you would rather leave him locked in the prison-tower, turn to **14**.

35

Fighting the force of the fearful snowstorm, which seems intent on barging its way into your home, you slam the door shut. You tense, for a moment, wondering if the noise will draw anyone else down from upstairs. But with the blizzard trapped beyond the walls of the house once more, and its keening wail muffled, the only sound you can hear coming from inside the house is the ticking of the grandfather clock.

If you want to examine the clock more closely, turn to **78**. If you would rather enter the sitting room, turn to **159**, or if you would prefer to enter the dining room, turn to **141**.

36

As it turned out, the Yule Lads were no match for you! (Record the code word *Krowded* on your Adventure Sheet.)

If you have the code word *Kretinous* already recorded on your Adventure Sheet, turn to **56**. If not, turn to **76**.

37

With a little persuasion, the silver key slides into the lock and, as it turns, you hear a distinct click.

Turn to **133**.

38

Remember, when you use the axe in battle you may add 1 bonus point when calculating your *Combat Rating*.

Now turn to **328**.

39

Cautiously you turn the handle of one of the doors, and it swings open. Peering through you see a candle-lit hall beyond, but no sign of another living soul. Stepping over the threshold, you close the door quietly behind you and start to sneak along the length of the hall, towards the pine door at the other end.

You have not gone far when, with your next step, you feel a floorboard give under your foot. You hear a click but, before you can do anything to save yourself, a trapdoor opens in the floor, directly beneath you.

Turn to **275**.

40

You dimly remember reading somewhere that the pure white wood of the mistletoe is anathema to demons and dark magic and so, grasping it firmly in both hands, you prepare to battle the polar bear. (In this battle you have the initiative.)

POLAR BEAR	COMBAT 10	ENDURANCE 13

If you manage to win three Combat Rounds, turn to **499** at once.

41

The imps dealt with, you make for the door by which they entered, and which you imagine must lead into the workshop itself.

So intent are you on the door, you do not notice the trapdoor hidden beneath a scattering of straw, halfway along the length of the stable. But you notice it when you step onto it, and it springs open beneath you!

Turn to **275**.

42

"Here," says the blacksmith, limping over to a cooking pot hung over the fire. He ladles some broth into a wooden bowl, before passing it to you, along with a spoon. "It'll warm you from the inside out."

You do not need to be told twice and you gulp down the steaming soup. It is very nourishing, full of root vegetables. (Gain 4 *Endurance* points.)

"Now," he says, as you pass the bowl back to him, "tell me what brings you here on a freezing Christmas Eve such as this."

Feeling you have nothing to lose, you relate the bizarre series of events that have brought you to this place at this time.

You are barely able to believe them yourself, when you share your story with the blacksmith; it all seems so fanciful. Like a twisted fairy tale.

When you are done telling your story, the blacksmith fixes you with eyes that shine like obsidian.

"It sounds like you fell foul of Krampus," he says, "and like as not, you're not the only one. He shouldn't be out and about on Christmas Eve, but if he is, then the Big Man himself could be in trouble."

"Don't worry," you tell the blacksmith, "I'm determined to stop Krampus and save Christmas!"

"I would go with you," the blacksmith says, "if it wasn't for this." He indicates his withered leg. "But I might be able to offer my aid another way."

If you have the Silver Sword, turn to **143**. If not, turn to **102**.

43

Where the Gingerbread Golem has gone big, you will go small.

Now no taller than a toffee apple, you dart across the kitchen, using the tables for cover again, unseen by the rampaging golem or the frantic goblin pastry chefs.

The effects of the box on your body do not last for long, but by the time you return to your normal size, you are on the cusp of making it to safety.

Turn to **300**.

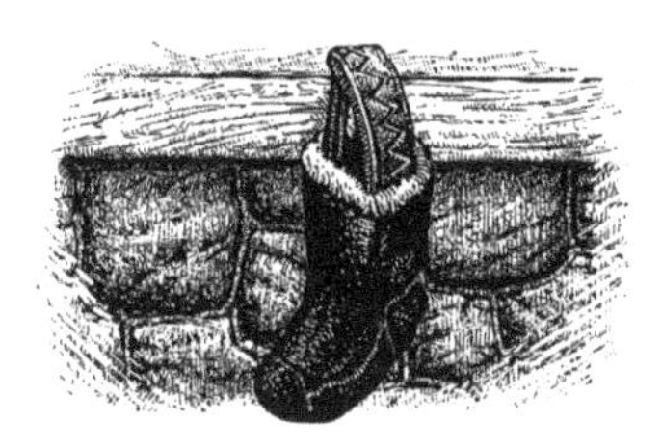

44

Cold water shock hits your body and you can't help but panic. As your dressing-gown and pyjamas become sodden, the icy waters close over you.

Carried along by the current, you find your way back to the surface blocked by ice. You punch at the glassy expanse, even as your lungs start to burn. But your efforts are futile; you cannot break the ice and you cannot hold your breath any longer.

You open your mouth in a silent scream, freezing water filling your lungs, and you drown beneath the frozen river.

Your adventure has come to an icy end.

The End

45

As the biting wind tugs at your hair, and the unremitting cold nips at the skin of your cheeks and the backs of your hands, you struggle on up the vertical ice-cliff.

Slowly but surely you climb higher and higher until you come to what appears to be a cave-mouth that has formed along a fault-line in the face of the glacier.

If you want to enter the ice cave, turn to **303**. If you would rather struggle on to the top, turn to **125**.

46

You are unable to free yourself from the imp's claws, which cut into the flesh of your shoulders, drawing blood. (Lose 2 *Endurance* points.)

However, as the winged devil flies on northwards, it begins to tire from having to carry you such a long way, until eventually, overcome by exhaustion, it lets go of you anyway.

You drop like a stone, but fortunately land in a deep snowdrift which breaks your fall. Clambering out of the drift, you realise that the forest is now half a league east of your current position, and you are, in fact, standing at the shore of the vast frozen lake.

Turn to **200**.

47

You start to run, hoping you can reach the far door before the Jack-in-the-Box pops open.

Take an Endurance test. If you pass the test, turn to **242**, but if you fail the test, turn to **81**.

48

Making it to the top of the drainpipe, you grab hold of the guttering and haul yourself onto the roof, as the blizzard howls around you.

And there, standing on the roof, is an ornately carved sleigh, painted a rich red and piled high with bulging sacks of presents, tethered behind a team of eight fully-grown reindeer! You can hardly believe your eyes!

But, as if the sleigh and reindeer weren't enough of a surprise, a tall, hunched figure, much of its form hidden by the fur-lined cloak it is wearing, is man-handling a large, and squirming, sack into the back of the sleigh. That done, it then jumps up into the driver's seat.

You are facing the back of the sleigh, so the snorting, stamping reindeer, and the sinister cloaked figure, are as yet unaware of your presence.

Taking up the reins, the figure tugs on them sharply and cracks the whip it is holding in its right hand. Startled, as one, the reindeer leap forwards, and the sleigh starts to slide across the tiles towards the edge of the roof.

Do you want to climb on board the sleigh before it takes off (turn to **13**), or do you think it would be more sensible to shimmy back down the drainpipe to the ground (turn to **62**)?

49

Turning your attention fully to the card, you find yourself looking at a painting of people, dressed like extras from a Dickens novel, enjoying a fair that is taking place on a frozen river, beside a stone bridge. There is a man roasting chestnuts on a brazier; women wrapped up warm against the cold, their hands buried in their mufflers; skating on the ice; a huddle of carol-singers; and cheeky urchins running this way and that through the crowd. Everyone is smiling and laughing, their faces glowing, their cheeks like rosy apples.

The painting is so life-like you can almost see the snow dusting the frozen river being blown into swirling eddies by the wind, while the scarves of the ladies are teased by the breeze, you can smell the chestnuts roasting on an open fire, and hear the dulcet singing of the carollers…

And then the cold wind is nipping at your nose and you find yourself there, at the frost fair, standing on the ice. You catch sight of a figure darting through the crowd, the same movement that drew your attention to the Christmas card in the first place.

Do you want to set off in pursuit of the figure (turn to **487**), or do you want to have a wander around the frost fair (turn to **64**)?

50

Kneeling before the altar, you close your eyes, and listen to the sound of your breathing. You feel like you could doze off at any moment, but then, in your mind's eye, you see…

A tower without a door, but clung all about with thick vines of ivy and the knotty branches of a holly rooted within the ice-cracked mortar between the stones…

Blinking yourself awake, you really think that you should be on your way again. However, if you haven't already tried to open the box, and would like to do so now, turn to **69**. Alternatively, you could leave the tower – turn to **381.**

51

Krampus tries to rake your flesh with his filthy claws, while you do your best to fend off your diabolical attacker. (Who has the initiative in this battle will depend upon how you got to this point.)

KRAMPUS	COMBAT 10	ENDURANCE 14

If you have the code word *Krazy* recorded on your Adventure Sheet, when calculating your *Combat Rating* you must subtract 1 point, because you are also driving the sleigh.

If you lose two consecutive Combat Rounds, turn to **31**. If you do not lose two consecutive Combat Rounds, after four Combat Rounds, if you are still alive, turn to **11**.

52

As the wolves race towards you, suddenly from out of the blizzard appears a huge white stag. Much bigger than a reindeer, its antlers spread out from its head like the branches of an ancient oak. The stag gives a bellow and, head down, charges the wolves, catching them on the prongs of its horns and tossing them into the air.

Giving your unanticipated saviour a shout of gratitude, you hurry away through the night and the snow, not bothered by wolves anymore.

Cross off one use of *The Pen is Mightier* special ability and turn to **83**.

53

Grabbing the pan from the stove, you hurl both it and its contents at the frozen hobgoblin.

Take an Agility test. If you pass the test, turn to **33**, but if you fail the test, turn to **188**.

54

Half-crouched in a stooped bow before the Snow Queen is a curious-looking figure. He looks like a hobgoblin, his frozen hair sticking out in jagged points, while icicles hang from the end of his long nose. He appears to be absolutely frozen, his features pinched and blue from the cold. In fact, you could almost believe he was made entirely from ice, if it wasn't for his penetrating blue eyes.

"So, Jack Frost, is it done?" the Queen asks in a voice as sharp as cut crystal.

"It is, your majesty," the hobgoblin replies.

Unseen by either of them, you listen in on their conversation.

"And where have you hidden the spear?" comes the Queen's second question.

"It is protected by both the holly and the ivy, in the north-east tower," comes Jack Frost's reply.

"And what of the sword? Where have you hidden that?"

"Far from here," the hobgoblin crows, a sparkling glint in his inhumanly human eyes. "Inside the ice cliff."

"And is that protected too?"

"Oh, yes, by the most abominable of guardians."

"The Lord of Misrule will be pleased," says the Snow Queen, a smile breaking her icy composure for a moment, "and we will both be held in high esteem when he takes the place of that doddering old saint. Now begone with you!"

Dismissed, Jack Frost transforms into a whirlwind of ice crystals which then blows out of the throne room.

So, at his Queen's behest, Jack Frost has hidden two weapons, one inside the castle, and one outside it. But why would she want him to do that? What power can they possess?

You are sure you will return to your normal size at any moment, so will you hurry back under the doors of the throne room and go in search of the spear (turn to **381**), or do you want to remain here and confront the Snow Queen, in the hope of finding out more about the weapons she has taken such pains to hide (turn to **154**)?

55

Pulling the belt of your dressing gown tight about your middle, keeping your head down against the force of the gale, you cross the threshold, pulling the front door closed behind you.

You can barely see your hand in front of your face as you step out into the snowstorm, the teeth of the wind snapping at you, threatening your skin with frostbite, and you are glad you have your bed socks on as well as your slippers.

But as you trudge through the wind-blown snow, you hear the jangling of a harness behind you – or is it the rattling of chains? – and turn in time to see a huge black shadow leap from the roof of your house to land in front of you.

Before you really know what is going on, a bony claw grabs hold of you and you are bundled into a large wicker basket the giant is carrying on its back, while the lid is slammed shut and fastened tight.

Turn to **420**.

56

You have got the better of not only the Yule Lads but also their matriarch, the giantess Gryla! (Regain 1 use of each of your special abilities *The Pen is Mightier* and *Naughty or Nice*.)

As you pick your way through the debris left in the aftermath of your battle with the trolls, you see a number of items that you are tempted to take with you: a bell, a lantern, and a pair of ice picks. (If you want to take any of the items, add them to the Equipment box on your Adventure Sheet.)

Making it to the door at last, you let yourself out. Pulling your dressing-gown tight about you, you set off again through the night-shrouded forest.

Turn to **473**.

57

The Yule Cat is all rippling muscle and savage, predatory intent, and will be a difficult foe to best in battle. (In this fight, you have the initiative.)

YULE CAT	COMBAT 9	ENDURANCE 8

If you manage to slay the carnivorous feline, turn to **27**.

58

Grabbing a large walnut from a bowl on the sideboard, you force it between the Nutcracker's snapping jaws, ramming it home with the heel of your hand. Something inside the mechanism gives and with a *PING!* the top of its head pops off.

Cross off one use of *The Pen is Mightier* special ability, and turn to **84**.

59

Taking one of the wolf heads in hand, you bring it down against the hard wood of the door three times.

A moment passes and then the mat on which you are standing, suddenly gives way as a trapdoor springs open beneath you.

Turn to **275**.

60

The succubus hisses and spits as she tries to rake your flesh with her terrible claws. You are forced to fight back against the demonic creature. (In this battle, you have the initiative.)

SUCCUBUS	COMBAT 7	ENDURANCE 7

If you manage to reduce the Succubus's *Endurance* score to 2 points or fewer, or after 4 Combat Rounds, whichever is sooner, turn to **180**.

61

If you have the Ledger of Souls with you, you will have a number associated with it; turn to that section number now. If not, turn to **74**.

62

Did you really just witness someone abducting Father Christmas? Or did you imagine it? Perhaps this is all just a disturbing dream anyway; it would explain so much of what has gone on.

Yawning, you trudge back inside the house and climb the stairs to bed. But as you pull the covers tight under your chin and drift off to sleep, you can't shake the feeling that Christmas will never be quite the same again…

Your adventure is over.

The End

63

The box might be the best way out of your dire predicament.

If you can remember what to do to go small, do it now. If you can't remember, or you change your mind about using the box at this juncture, return to **377** and try something else.

64

You are enraptured by the sights and sounds of the fair, from the brightly-coloured bunting of a toymaker's stall to the cries of hawkers and hustlers. The delicious smell of the roasting chestnuts sets your mouth watering, and you can see games of chance and skill that are causing the people gathered hereabouts much merriment and excitement.

"You look like you could do with something warm inside you," says the man in charge of the roast chestnuts.

"But I don't have any money," you tell him.

"Are you sure about that?" he asks.

Putting your hand into the pocket of your dressing gown you are surprised to find three shilling coins there. (Add the 3 Shillings to your Adventure Sheet.)

"They're one shilling a bag," says the man, indicating the bagged up roast chestnuts with a nod of his head.

If you want to spend 1 Shilling to buy a bag, turn to **86**. If you politely decline and move on through the fair, turn to **106**.

65

Scaling the glacier is not only physically exhausting, it is also made doubly difficult by the fact that you have to cling onto the freezing structure of the ice-cliff by your fingertips. In the end, that combination just proves to be too challenging and, as you are reaching for a higher hand-hold, you lose your grip on the ice-cliff, tumbling back down to the bottom.

You land in the snow, but do not get away entirely unscathed.

Roll one die and add 1. Deduct this many *Endurance* points. (Alternatively, pick a card and deduct its face value from your *Endurance* score, unless it is 8 or above or a picture card, in which case deduct 7 points from your *Endurance* score.)

If you still alive, knowing that you have no other choice but to try to scale the ice-cliff again, you look for an alternative route up and commence your climb again.

Turn to **45**.

66

Leaving the supervisor's office, you enter what you realise is an entrance hall. Other doors lead from it to other parts of the complex, but you start to wonder whether Father Christmas is even inside the building. Your suspicions are confirmed when you realise that one of the large double doors leading outside is slightly ajar.

Making your way to the door, you peer out into the biting cold night. And then you see something that wasn't there when you first arrived at the workshop.

Some two hundred yards away, you can see flames flickering at the top of a snow-covered hill and strange capering figures, while overhead, ragged black shapes circle the sky beneath the rippling green coruscation of the Northern Lights.

Determined to find out what is going on, you set off into the snow once more.

If you have the code word *Kold* recorded on your Adventure Sheet, turn to **356**. If not, turn to **483**.

67

Exhausted as you are, after all your endeavours, your reactions are dulled and so you do not get out of the way in time. You fall into the yawning gulf, plunging into the hellish pit beneath, never to be seen again.

Your adventure ends here, with you descending into Hell.

The End

68

You enter a room that is slightly larger than the last, dominated by a table bearing the largest, roundest Christmas pudding you have ever seen. As the door closes behind you, it triggers a Heath Robinson-esque contraption, which empties a saucepan of burning brandy over the bomb.

As the pudding is licked by blue flames, you become aware of a hissing sound, and you see that the sprig of holly stuck into the top is sparking furiously. Only it's not really a sprig of holly – it's a fuse!

Fearing the worst, you run for the door on the far side of the room, desperate to escape before the pudding can explode.

If you want to use the *Naughty or Nice* special ability, and you still can, turn to **255**. If not, turn to **276**.

69

The box is not locked and opens with ease. Lying inside it is a large silver key, embossed with the number '37'. Having pocketed the key, what would you like to do next?

Do you want to spend a minute alone with your thoughts, if you haven't already (turn to **50**), or would you prefer to leave the chapel-tower without further delay (turn to **381**)?

70

As you watch the whirling, repetitive movements of the Snapdragon, you realise that one of the floorboards at your feet is loose. Exerting only a little effort, you are able to prise it up.

You thrust the plank of wood into the wooden inner workings of the automaton, the co-opted floorboard jamming the gears, and the whole mechanism grinds to a halt.

Cross off one use of *The Pen is Mightier* special ability and turn to **190**.

71

With you and Krampus preoccupied with what each other are doing, no one is paying attention to the reindeer or in which direction they are taking the sleigh.

Cross off one use of *Naughty or Nice* special ability and then turn to **11**.

72

If you have found a key, somewhere in the castle, that you think might unlock the door, turn to the number stamped on it. If not, but you have a set of Lockpicks, and want to try to open the door using these, turn to **111**. If you have neither key nor lockpicks, turn to **92**.

73

You are going to have to act fast. What do you want to do?

If you want to throw the pan of mulled wine at the hobgoblin, turn to **53**. If you want to simply flee from it, turn to **218**.

74

With which weapon do you intend to finish the Christmas Devil?

The Blacksmith's Axe?	Turn to **38**.
The Silver Sword?	Turn to **249**.
The Ice Sword Frostbite?	Turn to **169**.
None of the above?	Turn to **328**.

75

Taking the large iron doorknocker in hand, you bang it against the door. You can make out the chatter of excited voices coming from the other side, and then hear the sound of heavy bolts being pulled back.

Slowly, the door opens a crack, and a hideous creature peers through the gap. It is no taller than you are, but hunched and misshapen. Its knuckles drag on the floor and it has a huge nose that is both long and pronounced.

The troll sniffs at you and then pulls a face.

"Who is it, Doorway-Sniffer?" comes a sharp voice from further back, inside the cave.

"Don't know," replies the troll. "Doesn't smell like anyone we know."

"Maybe they've come for supper," another disembodied voice suggests.

"Good point," says the troll, glancing back over his shoulder, and then to you, "Please, come in, come in!"

Throwing open the door, the curious creature ushers you inside, before slamming the portal shut behind you. You stare in astonishment at the scene that greets you within.

The cave has been furnished as if it's someone's home. There is a long table, dressers are pushed up against the walls, and you can see several bunk beds. At the back of the cave a large cauldron of water has been set to boil over a large fire, the smoke from which disappears up a chimney breast that has been built into the cave wall.

But most astonishing of all are the cave's inhabitants. It is full of more of the ugly, troll-like beings – you count thirteen in all – while standing beside the bubbling cauldron is an ogress, who must be at least twice as tall as you are.

The giantess fixes you with a flint-hard stare and she offers you a broken-toothed smile.

"Who's been a naughty-naughty then?" she cackles, and half a dozen of the trolls seize hold of you.

If you are in possession of the Box of Delights, turn to **115**. If not, turn to **254**.

76

"My boys! My poor boys!" the giantess screams. "My poor lads!"

Snatching up a cleaver as big as an axe, she closes the space between the two of you in only a few strides.

"Why, I'll butcher you like the dog you are!" she roars.

How will you respond to such threatening behaviour? Will you:

Use *The Pen is Mightier* special ability?	Turn to **96**.
Use your *Naughty or Nice* special ability?	Turn to **146**.
Prepare to defend yourself?	Turn to **116**.

77

Hissing and spitting like a fury, the carnivorous feline bares its claws, ready to strike you down and besmirch the pristine snow with your rich red blood.

If you want to use *The Pen is Mightier* special ability now, turn to **97**. If not, turn to **57**.

78

You approach the long case of the looming clock and peer through the gloom at its face. The hands of the clock read two minutes after midnight, but you are sure you heard it chime thirteen.

You stare at the scene visible through the cut-out window in the faceplate that shows a smiling moon peeping out between clouds and twinkling stars. But as you turn away from the clock again, out of the corner of your eye, you fancy you see something fly across the face of the painted moon.

Before you have a chance to take another look, a crash from the kitchen has you turning your attention towards the door at the far end of the hall.

Your pulse quickens again. Someone, or some*thing*, is in the kitchen.

If you want to run back up to your room, jump back into bed and hide under the covers, turn to **98**. If not, turn to **129**.

79

You pull hard on the bell-pull, and the mat on which you are standing suddenly gives way as a trapdoor opens beneath you.

Turn to **275**.

80

The book suddenly opens, as if with a will of its own, and your eyes alight on a page that doesn't contain a list of names. Instead, written on it in an ancient gothic hand is an invocation in Latin.

"Light the candle, ring the bell, and read the invocation!" Father Christmas tells you.

Dropping the open book on the ground, you light the candle from one of the blazing braziers, holding it in one hand as you ring the bell in the other, and, in as loud a voice as you can manage, you do your best to read the Latin incantation.

As you do so, Krampus starts to howl and tries to cover his ears with his clawed hands, but it doesn't seem to do anything to lessen his agony.

When you have finished reading the invocation, Father Christmas calls out to your again. "Read it again, and keep reading it. Do not stop!"

You do as he says. And as you read, the ground suddenly splits apart, as a wide fissure opens in the earth. You are struck by a gust of hot air rising from its infernal depths, but it isn't you who is sent tumbling into the pit. With a final braying scream of frustration, rage and pain, it is Krampus who is sent plummeting into the hellish abyss.

Turn to **500**.

81

As you run past it, the Jack-in-the-Box springs open and a demented jester-like character, with an over-large smile splitting its porcelain face, flies out. The jester has stiletto-blades for fingers, and below its waist there is nothing by a cloth-covered uncoiled spring.

A horrible, high-pitched giggle, running on repeat, comes from somewhere inside its chest, rather than its insanely leering mouth, as the Jack-in-the-Box lurches for you. As you try to dodge the sweep of its stiletto-blade fingers, you trip and go sprawling on the floor. (Lose 2 *Endurance* points.)

If you want to employ *The Pen is Mightier* special ability, turn to **209**. If not, turn to **101**.

82

A burning log pops, and sends a spark flying from the fire that lands on the Perchta's tattered dress, which immediately bursts into flames. As it burns, the horrible thing's insane giggling only reaches new heights of hysteria until the puppet is nothing more than a blackened husk smouldering in the grate.

Turn to **66**.

83

You finally make it to the far side of the lake, without falling foul of any other creatures that might be looking for prey on this freezing night.

Turn to **446**.

84

You stare at the Nutcracker, now lying broken on the floor – and still once more – your heart pounding inside your chest and your hands shaking. What is going on?

Turn to **206**.

85

You start to pelt it with a profusion of projectiles – anything you can get your hands on, from custard tarts and hazelnut whirls, to whole stollen and peppermint candy canes. But your assault does nothing to slow the Gingerbread Golem's advance; if anything, it only serves to make it even angrier.

In its rage, the Golem raises one foot and stamps down hard on the floor. Several terracotta tiles crack under the force of the blow and a powerful tremor passes through the ground.

Take an Agility test. If you pass the test, turn to **167**, but if you fail the test, turn to **105**.

86

Paying the man, you take a bag from the brazier and tuck in. The roast chestnuts are both delicious and warming.

Gain 3 *Endurance* points and then turn to **106**.

87

The gingerbread men turn their jelly sweet noses up at your offering, but it's too late to try to retrieve the wasted food items now.

Cross off 1 Meal and turn to **419**.

88

Casually strolling over to the cauldron, as if you're not about to become the main ingredient of the stew, you drop the stone into the pot.

"You haven't tasted anything until you've tasted stone stew," you tell the expectant trolls.

Taking the ladle from the giantess, you give the concoction a stir, and then taste a little of the bubbling broth yourself.

"Hmm, delicious. But it needs a little seasoning," you say. "Do you have any salt and pepper?"

One of the trolls passes you a salt cellar, while another passes you a pepper grinder, and they watch intently as you season the stock.

You leave it to simmer for a few moments before tasting it again.

"Do you know what goes really well with stone stew? Cabbage. Or, failing that, sprouts."

Some sprouts are duly brought to the pot and added to the mixture.

"Do you have any onions?" you ask, after tasting the bubbling broth again.

And so some chopped onions are added to the cauldron. And then some chopped leeks, and diced turnip, and a couple of parsnips go into the pot, and even a few rashers of bacon, with you tasting the stock after each ingredient is added. (Add 2 *Endurance* points.)

Finally, you turn to the giantess and, passing her the ladle, ask, "What do you think of that?"

And as she leans forward over the huge cauldron, to taste the broth you have made, you give her an almighty shove.

Take an Endurance test. If you pass the test, turn to **491**, but if you fail the test, turn to **471**.

89

The door to the south-west tower is carved with a cross. Entering the tower, you ascend a spiral staircase to a small chapel. Upon an altar, under a stained glass window depicting a single shining star hanging in a velvet black sky above a small desert town, is a plain wooden box.

Now that you are inside the peaceful chapel, do you want to kneel before the altar and spend a minute alone with your thoughts (turn to **50**), do you want to open the box (turn to **69**), or would you prefer to leave the chapel-tower immediately (turn to **381**)?

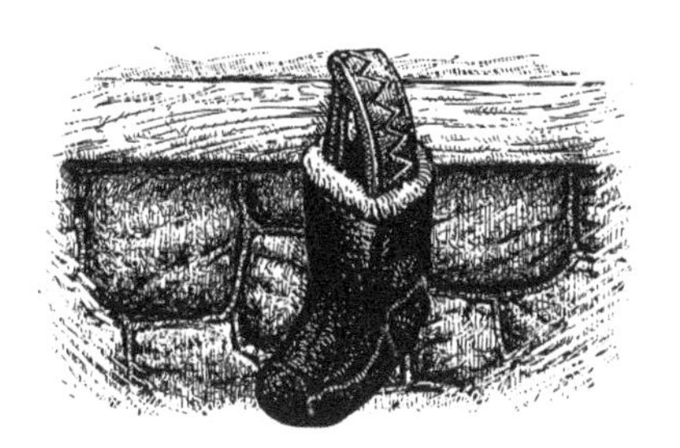

90

Flapping its wings, the Perchta flies out of your reach. Still giggling insanely, it throws a handful of what looks like glitter over the Christmas tree before flying across the room to the fireplace, and disappearing up the chimney.

But your attention is back on the tree in an instant as it becomes suffused with an eerie luminescence. The baubles and other decorations adorning it rattle and jangle as its branches start to twitch.

Its roots bursting from the pot in which it has been planted, it advances towards you, the exposed roots acting as clumsy feet, while a pair of branches become tentacle-like arms. Within the pine needles you even think you can see the impression of a snarling mouth and two empty eye-sockets.

If you want to employ *The Pen is Mightier* special ability now, cross off one use and turn to **120**. If not, you have no choice but to fight the animated Christmas tree. (In this battle, the Dubik has the initiative.)

DUBIK	COMBAT 8	ENDURANCE 8

If you win your battle with the evil spirit animating the tree, turn to **120**.

91

You pull hard on the reins and the sleigh slews sideways, sending the devil sliding out of the driver's seat. Your actions would have had him slide out of the sleigh completely, if it wasn't for the fact that he has managed to grab hold of a carved lantern mount.

Cross off one use of *The Pen is Mightier* special ability and then turn to **11**.

92

"Have you tried searching the other towers?" Venceslav asks. "The key must be hidden somewhere. In the keep, perhaps?"

Unable to help the dethroned king at the present time, you decide to take his advice and search elsewhere.

If you find a key while you are searching the castle, and want to return to the north-west tower to free the prisoner, ignore the instructions given at that point in the adventure and turn to the number stamped on the key instead. But for now, turn to **381**.

93

In a flash of inspiration, you grab the pan of warming wine from the stove and hurl it at the frozen hobgoblin.

Cross off one use of your *The Pen is Mightier* special ability and turn to **33**.

94

The spear flies straight and true and finds its target, hitting the shaggy-haired half-goat, half-man demon in the chest. Krampus gives a bleating cry and topples backwards onto the snowy ground.

Father Christmas still lies at the centre of the pentagram, and surely the longer he remains like that, the more his power will weaken.

As if he has read your mind, you hear Father Christmas call out in a booming voice, "Don't worry about me! See to the fiend first!"

Do you want to ignore the big man's wishes and help Father Christmas first (turn to **122**), or do you want to do as he says and check that Krampus really is dead (turn to **248**)?

95

Pushing the knob on the top of the box to the right, you rapidly shrink – your clothes and possessions shrinking with you, as the furniture in the room and the trolls seem to grow, all becoming giants – until you are the size of a cockroach!

Your would-be captors start to shriek at each other, demanding to know where you've gone. Now that you are tiny, and free of the trolls' clutches, you sprint for cover under a dresser. There you see a crack in the cave wall, and feeling the cold breeze blowing from it tells you that it must lead outside.

Not wanting to remain in the trolls' cave a moment longer, you make for the fissure. But before you can reach it, something scampers into your path, blocking your way out.

It is a rat, only to you it now appears to be as big as an elephant! The rodent gives a shrill squeak, baring long, yellow, chisel-like teeth, and goes for you.

If you want to use *The Pen is Mightier* special ability, and still can, turn to **135**. If not, turn to **174**.

96

"What's all this noise?" comes another voice from the back of the cave, and you realise for the first time that there is someone else here. "What is it, wife? Is supper ready yet?"

It is Gryla's husband, the giant Leppaludi.

"It will be, once I've jointed this little blighter and thrown it in the pot."

As the repulsively ugly giant lumbers into view, scratching his backside with one hand, while picking at a boil on his nose with the other, Gryla turns to greet him, and you seize your chance to get away from her.

Cross off one use of *The Pen is Mightier* special ability and turn to **216**.

97

As the cat pounces, you duck and, as it flies over your head, grab hold.

Now that you have the cat by the tail, you use its momentum to swing it into the side of the tree stump, where a protruding, wooden spike goes straight through its eye and into its brain, killing it instantly.

Cross off one use of *The Pen is Mightier* special ability and then turn to **27**.

98

You dread to think who can have invaded your home on Christmas Eve, but you don't want to hang about to find out either.

Taking the stairs two at a time, you hurry back to your bedroom, slamming the door behind you, and jump into bed. Pulling the bedclothes tight over your head, you lie there, your over-excited heartbeat pounding in your ears.

And as you lie there, ears straining, waiting for the feeling of dread and your hammering pulse to subside, you hear a heavy tread on the stairs, and then the creak of a floorboard outside your door.

It's all you can do not to let out a whimper of fear as the handle turns and the door opens.

The close air of your bedroom becomes thick with the musky smell of a stable, and you sense the tremors of something large and hunched moving about the room, chains slowly clanking as it does so.

(Lose 1 *Combat* point from fear.)

You are rigid under the covers, paralysed with fear. And then suddenly the bedclothes are yanked back and in the night-gloom of your room you nonetheless become aware of a huge shadow looming over you.

You see the silhouette of a great clawed hand descend, and before you really know what's going on, it snatches you from the bed and bundles you into the large wicker basket it is carrying on its back, slamming the lid shut and fastening it tight.

Turn to **420**.

99

You try to throw yourself out of the way but one of the erratic blasts clips your arm. (Lose 2 *Endurance* points.)

You realise that your only hope of getting out of here alive is to tackle the robot head on, and so run directly towards it.

The power cells of its ray guns depleted, the robot casts the weapons aside, raising its snapping pincer-claws threateningly.

If you want to employ *The Pen is Mightier* special ability now, and you still can, turn to **149**. If not, make a note that in the battle to come the robot has the initiative and turn to **179**.

100

You rush towards the edifice, your heart pounding in your chest, running as fast as the deep snow will allow. Before you stands the impressive entrance to the workshop – with lanterns hanging beside the huge, carved double doors – but off to the left you can see what appear to be the stables where Father Christmas must keep his reindeer.

Do you want to approach the workshop via the main entrance (turn to **119**), or would you rather sneak around the side of the building and try to gain access through the stables (turn to **162**)?

101

You have no choice but to defend yourself against the demonic jester. (The Jack-in-the-Box has the initiative in this battle.)

JACK-IN-THE-BOX	COMBAT 7	ENDURANCE 8

If you manage to defeat the jester, turn to **229**.

102

"These polar climes are a hazard to any traveller, and not just because of the cold," the blacksmith says. "How do you intend to defend yourself, should you run into any opposition?"

"I have my wits," you say. "They've got me this far."

"But what you really need is a weapon," the blacksmith says, "for those times when you cannot beat your foes by brains alone. Here, take this."

He offers you the axe he clearly uses to chop the wood for the fire, and you see no reason not to accept it.

(Record the Blacksmith's Axe on your Adventure Sheet and make a note that when you use it in battle, you may add 1 point to your *Combat Rating*.)

Suddenly there comes a knock at the door, startling you.

"Who's there?" demands the blacksmith, getting to his feet.

Turn to **252**.

103

You have had a long, hard journey to reach Santa's workshop this cold Christmas Eve, and, your mouth watering already, you cannot resist tucking in. You load a plate with vegetables and cranberry sauce, finally picking up a carving knife to carve yourself some of the turkey, which you fully intend to smother with the rich gravy.

However, the instant the knife breaks the crisp skin of the fowl, the turkey twitches and springs into the air. Despite having no head or feet, the cooked bird stomps towards you on the stumps of its legs, as if intent on teaching you a lesson in vegetarianism.

If you want to use *The Pen is Mightier* special ability, and you still can, turn to **153**. If not, turn to **183**.

104

The table has been set, with the finest silver cutlery and folded linen napkins, ready for Christmas dinner. But you are appalled to find that the tablecloth itself is filthy. It appears to be covered in soot! And lying on a mat in the centre of the table – the spot reserved for the turkey – is a huge cracker, the largest you've ever seen, with a bright red tag that reads simply, "Pull Me!"

If you want to pull the cracker, turn to **123**. If you would rather leave well enough alone, turn to **184**.

105

The shuddering quake causes you to lose your balance and fall to the floor.

If you end up having to fight the Gingerbread Golem, you must do so with your *Combat Rating* reduced by 2 points for the first round of the battle as you struggle to get to your feet.

Now turn to **264**.

106

"Roll up! Roll up! Try your luck!" comes a hawker's cry that attracts your attention. "Could you be the next Robin 'ood? Two Shillings a go! Three arrers, three chances! Get one in the gold and win a prize!"

A large lady, wrapped in shawls and wearing a bonnet, is in charge of the stall. It is a game of skill rather than one of chance; an archery challenge.

"Three arrers, two shillings, one in the gold!" shouts the woman.

If you want to try your hand at the archery challenge, turn to **126**. If not, turn to **241**.

107

As they advance towards you, the gingerbread men come together in a huddle and before your very eyes merge their bodies together. As they do so, the now shapeless lump of gingerbread starts to swell and grow.

In no time at all the doughy mass is as tall as you are, and limbs extrude from the giant ball of gingerbread as it takes on a recognisably humanoid form once again.

Cross off one use of your *Naughty or Nice* special ability and turn to **377**.

108

Another room, another two very similar doors, but this time it is a statement and not a question that has been painted on the wall:

No two snowflakes can ever be identical.

On one door has been painted the word 'True' and on the other, 'False'. But which one will you choose?

'True'? Turn to **124**.

'False'? Turn to **68**.

109

You fill a goblet from the wassail bowl and gulp down the warming drink. However, a moment later, you are vomiting it all up again!

Unbeknownst to you, someone has added the juice of mistletoe berries to the concoction, poisoning you in the process!

(Lose 4 *Endurance* points.)

Not feeling like anything to eat now, you leave the tower as quickly as you can.

Turn to **381**.

110

"Come in out of the cold," you tell the young woman, and she shuffles inside, shivering from being out in the freezing night. "Here, have my seat by the fire and warm yourself."

"Thank you kindly, stranger," she says, "but it's all right, your blood will warm me well enough."

Suddenly she throws herself at you, her fingernails becoming savage claws, while her beautiful visage is subsumed by a twisted demonic leer.

If you want to use *The Pen is Mightier* special ability, cross off one use and turn to **180**. If not, turn to **150**.

111

As you work the picks within the lock, one of them slips and digs into the palm of your hand.

(Lose 1 *Endurance* point and 1 *Combat* point, as a result of the injury.)

However, in the end you at least manage to unlock the cell door.

Turn to **133**.

112

Unlatching the window, you push it open, and the sprite bounds through into the cottage. His intentions immediately become plain as he goes to grab you with fingers that are little more than icy needles.

How do you want to defend yourself?

Use *The Pen is Mightier special ability?* *Turn to* **93**.

Fight back? Turn to **268**.

Try something else? Turn to **73**.

113

You still need to somehow force the sleigh back down to the ground, if you are to escape from it without throwing yourself over the side thousands of feet up in the air.

Clouds, heavy with snow, rush past overhead, beneath a midnight blue velvet sky, scattered with a million twinkling stars, as you ponder the best course of action to follow.

Will you:

Try to wrest control of the sleigh from its driver? Turn to **340**.

Attack the driver? Turn to **360**.

114

As the opening fissure races towards you, you throw yourself out of the way. Picking yourself up again quickly, you charge at Krampus.

If you want to use *The Pen is Mightier* special ability now, and you still can, turn to **220**.

If not, continue your battle with the Christmas Devil, in which you now have the initiative, and if you are victorious in your battle with the anti-Santa, turn to **181**.

115

The polished wooden box the Punch and Judy Man gave you might be your only hope. Managing to wrest one arm free of the trolls, you quickly pull it from the pocket of your dressing-gown.

If you can remember what to do to go small, and you want to, do it now. If you can't remember, or you don't want to use the box now, turn to **254**.

116

Waving the filthy cleaver before her, the giantess is clearly determined to have you end up in her pot. (In this battle, Gryla has the initiative.)

GRYLA	COMBAT 8	ENDURANCE 10

If you win the battle with the trolls' mother, turn to **216**.

117

The Yule Cat is all rippling muscle and savage, predatory intent, and will be a difficult foe to best in battle. (In this fight, the Yule Cat has the initiative.)

YULE CAT	COMBAT 9	ENDURANCE 8

If you manage to slay the carnivorous feline, turn to **27**.

118

"Oh, go on, Mama," says a troll, who is abnormally short, compared to his brethren. "Let it out. It is Christmas, after all. Please."

"All right then, Stubby," says the giantess, softening. "But only 'cos you asked so nicely. Go on, Door-Slammer," she instructs the troll holding the keys, "open the cage and let our guest out."

Door-Slammer does as instructed, and deciding that you're not going to get a better opportunity than this to escape, you burst out of the cage and race for the circular door.

Turn to **199**.

119

Climbing the steps to the ornate wooden porch, passing snow-dusted stone statues of rampant heraldic reindeer, you come to a halt before the grand double doors. In front of you is a large welcome mat, with the words 'Season's Greetings' on it.

Beside the entrance hangs a bell-pull, while large brass knockers, fashioned in the shape of snarling wolves' heads, are fixed to the doors themselves.

How will you attempt to gain access to the building? Do you want to:

Tug firmly on the bell-pull?	Turn to **79**.
Bang on the door with one of the wolf's head door knockers?	Turn to **59**.
See if you can open the door, without first announcing your arrival?	Turn to **39**.

120

Pulling free of the Christmas tree's clutches, you hurl yourself out of the sitting room and through the door that leads into the kitchen.

Turn to **5**.

121

With a scream of rending metal and shearing axles, something somewhere within the production line suffers a catastrophic failure and the clattering conveyor unravels, as gears jam and the belt is ripped apart.

Screams of panic fill the workshop as Satan's little helpers fall victim to the self-destructing machinery.

Finding yourself at the foot of a wooden staircase, with nowhere else to go, you run up it to escape the encroaching chaos, taking the stairs two at a time, and throw yourself through the pair of finely-carved doors at the top.

Turn to **485**.

122

"What are you doing, you fool?" chides the old bearded fellow as you hurry to help him, kneeling down in the snow, as you set about loosening his bonds. "I told you to check on Krampus!"

His ancient sparkling eyes suddenly widen and he cries, "Look out!"

But his warning comes too late.

As you turn to see what Father Christmas has set eyes on, you receive a vicious blow to the side of the head. Reeling, you stagger to your feet. Your vision swimming, you see the goat-leggéd one standing there, a gaping wound in his shoulder, and the mistletoe spear grasped tightly in both hands. Indeed, it looks like Krampus intends to kill you with it!

And so it has come to this – you have no choice but to engage the Christmas Devil in single combat!

Lose 2 *Endurance* points and 1 *Combat* point, record the code word *Kritical* on your Adventure Sheet, and if you are still alive, only then turn to **74**.

123

Lifting the cracker from the centre of the table – it really is quite heavy – you take hold of it at both ends, and, wincing in anticipation of the bang that is surely to come, pull hard.

But the snap, when it comes, is more like the concussive boom of a bomb going off, and you are thrown across the room by the blast!

Roll one die and add 1. Deduct this many *Endurance* points. (Alternatively, pick a card and deduct its face value from your *Endurance* score, unless it is 8 or above or a picture card, in which case deduct 7 points from your *Endurance* score.)

Incredibly, the sound of the cracker exploding still doesn't appear to have woken anyone else and drawn them down from upstairs.

You pick yourself up, and dust yourself down. Looking in the mirror, by the white-blue glow of the icicle lights, you see that the front of your dressing gown is now black with soot, as is your face.

And then you spot something lying on the floor. It is the gift that was inside the cracker: a set of lockpicks.

If you want to take the Lockpicks, record them on your Equipment list and then turn to **206**.

124

Pulling open the door, you confidently step through, and let it slam shut again behind you.

Turn to **7**.

125

You struggle on, and just as your arms start shaking with the effort, you haul yourself onto the top of the glacier. (Deduct 1 point from your *Endurance* score, unless that would take your *Endurance* score to zero.)

If you have the code word *Kold* written down on your Adventure Sheet, turn to **145**. If not, turn to **185**.

126

Paying the woman the required 2 Shillings, you pick up the bow and the three arrows she lays out for you in return for your coins. Nocking the first shaft to the string, you draw it back until your arm is shaking with the effort, take aim, and then you loose the arrow.

Take 3 Combat tests! As soon as you pass one, turn to **201**. However, if you fail all three tests, turn to **221**.

127

Taking the piece you broke off from the bench outside the gingerbread cottage in the forest, you throw it in front of the grimacing guardians. One of the tiny biscuit people picks it up, gives it a sniff, and then starts to eat it. But as it does so, something strange happens.

The magic that the gingerbread from the cottage is imbued with starts to work on the gingerbread man, and it begins to grow. In no time at all it is as tall as you are, absorbing any other gingerbread men that get too close to its rapidly swelling body.

In no time at all, the gingerbread man is twice as tall as you, and it is still growing!

Cross off the Gingerbread, as well as 1 Meal, and turn to **377**.

128

You tuck into a hearty meal of poached carp and prunes, and spiced porridge, which leaves you feeling revitalised and reenergised.

(Gain 4 *Endurance* points.)

If you want, you may take another 2 Meals' worth of food from the feast laid out on the table.

When you are done, do you want to wash it all down with a glass of something warming (turn to **109**), or would you prefer leave the tower and search elsewhere (turn to **381**)?

129

Your heart hammering against the cage of your ribs, you decide what to do next. Do you want to hide in one of the rooms downstairs, or confront whoever is skulking about in the kitchen?

Will you:

Enter the sitting room?	Turn to **159**.
Enter the dining room?	Turn to **141**.
Enter the kitchen?	Turn to **5**.

130

You heart thumping against your ribs in fear, you try to keep low and creep through the blizzard, hoping that the wolves don't see you, and that the crunching of your footsteps on the snow doesn't have them pricking up their ears.

If you have the word *Krumbly* recorded on your Adventure Sheet, turn to **289**. If not, turn to **315**.

131

A bolt of lightning suddenly splits the sky, and the snowstorm, asunder. Just at that moment, the other's hood falls back revealing his horrible face for the first time.

It is the demonic leer of some hideous amalgam of man and beast, with the caprine eyes of a goat, wolfish fangs, and long curling horns. A prehensile tongue whips from the creature's mouth, moving as if with a life of its own and a guttural cackle rises from the devil's throat.

"What do we have here? A devious spy?
Well Krampus says it's your time to die!"

And with that, the fiend makes a grab for you.

How do you want to respond? Will you:

Use your *The Pen is Mightier* special ability (if you can)?	Turn to **91**.
Use your *Naughty or Nice* special ability (if you can)?	Turn to **71**.
Fight back against Krampus?	Turn to **51**.

132

"Curse you then!" snaps the creature, in a voice that sounds like the cracking of ice on a pond. "May the north wind freeze the blood in your veins!"

Record the code word *Krafty* on your Adventure Sheet, and then turn to **355**.

133

"Thank you! Oh, thank you!" Venceslav cries, hurrying out of the cell before you can change your mind and shut him in again.

The cell he has been living in, for goodness knows how long, is a dank affair, with mouldering straw on the floor and frost covering the walls. The only illumination comes from the moon shining in through a small stained glass window, high up in the tower – and inaccessible to anyone imprisoned inside the cell – that depicts three ships in full sale riding the stormy waves of a stylised sea.

"So now we must oust the Snow Queen from your castle and reclaim your throne," you tell the deposed king.

"Yes, about that…" he says, awkwardly ringing his hands. "I don't actually think I'm up to it. But if that's what you want to do, go for it!" And with that he scampers out of the prison-tower and away across the courtyard, with you just watching his retreating back in disbelief.

Perhaps it's time you left this cursed castle too.

Record the code word *Krowned* on your Adventure Sheet and then turn to **381**.

134

Suddenly the *chung-chung* of a shockwave echoes across the lake and the ice only a few stride-lengths ahead of you fractures, as a tangle of tentacles bursts through from beneath. The elongated, purple, squid-like arms are reaching for you, and you are forced to take evasive action.

You dodge out of the way of the lashing tentacles, only for them to be withdrawn and the ice rupture elsewhere, nearby, as they re-emerge in a welter of gelid water.

Turn to **182**.

135

Suddenly you are aware of a pair of orange glowing eyes peering at you, and then a large paw comes sweeping in under the dresser, with claws unsheathed. The rat lets out a squeak of pain and fear as the cat catches hold of its hairless tail, and drags it out.

Turn to **204**.

136

You are slightly surprised to find the precious object the old Punch and Judy Man gave you still in your dressing-gown pocket – so you really did visit the frost fair, somehow! – and study the smooth wooden box.

If you know what you need to do to go swift, and you want to, do it now. If you don't know, or you don't want to, turn to **62**.

137

The creature you are facing is the savage Yule Cat, a lethal predator that stalks the winter wilderness hunting for those unfortunate wretches who have not received any new clothes for Christmas.

If you want to use *The Pen is Mightier* special ability now, turn to **97**. If not, turn to **117**.

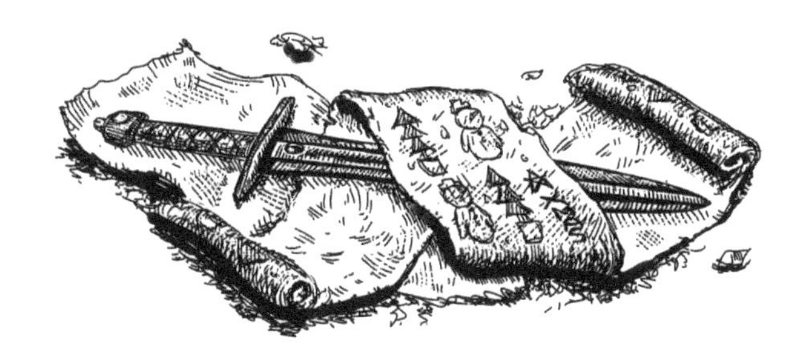

138

"You're sorry, are you?" laughs the giantess. "What good is sorry to us? We can't eat 'sorry', can we?"

You clearly can't appeal to her better nature, probably because she doesn't have one, so what do you want to try now?

Will you:

Use the Box of Delights (if you have it)?	Turn to **311**.
Use a set of Lockpicks (if you have some)?	Turn to **371**.
Offer your captors a drink of Schnapps (if you have some)?	Turn to **391**.
Offer your captors some Carrots (if you have some)?	Turn to **451**.
Plead with the trolls to let you go?	Turn to **2**.
Use your *Naughty or Nice* special ability, if you still can?	Turn to **118**.
Wait and see what happens?	Turn to **158**.

139

The polar bear suddenly locks eyes with you, and you feel that you can see something of the cursed king in its soulful stare.

Giving another bellow, the beast suddenly breaks off its charging attack, turns tail and lollops away into the night and the snow, leaving you gasping for breath and your heart racing like a steam locomotive.

When you finally feel ready to resume your journey, no longer fearing that the bear might pick up your scent and come back for you, you set off again, travelling north towards the dark teeth of the mountains.

Turn to **244**.

140

If you are going to get past the Snapdragon, you are going to have to fend off its flailing blows as best you can.

Take a Combat test. If you pass the test, turn to **190**, but if you fail the test, turn to **160**.

141

It is dark in the dining room, but someone has forgotten to turn off the string of icicle-shaped bulbs adorning the mirror that hangs on one wall, and this provides enough light for you to effectively navigate the room. This room has been almost as exuberantly decorated as the sitting room; there are Christmas cards, sprigs of holly and bunches of mistletoe, and a small tree stands in one corner. On top of that, everything that was already in the room has been garlanded with tinsel and lengths of Christmas bunting.

At the far end of the dining room, the door leading into the kitchen is closed, but there is something about the atmosphere here that gives you the impression something has been disturbed, and you feel compelled to investigate.

Do you want to:

Search the sideboard for clues?	Turn to **161**.
Examine the dining table itself?	Turn to **104**.
Look at the decorations adorning the room?	Turn to **184**.

142

You boldly step through the door, which slams shut again behind you.

Roll one die (or pick a card). If the number rolled is odd (or the card is red), turn to **253**. If the number rolled is even (or the card is black), turn to **343**.

143

"These polar climes are a hazard to any traveller, and not just because of the cold," the blacksmith says. "How do you intend to defend yourself, should you run into any opposition?"

"I have this," you say, pulling the Silver Sword from where it is tucked into the belt of your dressing-gown.

"Ah," the man says, his obsidian eyes glittering in the firelight that reflects from the gleaming blade, "I think I can do something with this. You sit here by the fire while I sharpen it against my whetstone."

If you agree to the blacksmith taking the sword to sharpen it, turn to **164**. If you would rather he didn't touch it, turn to **210**.

144

Undoing the cord, you pull the sack open and are surprised to find yourself looking down into a softly-lined face, with rosy red cheeks, a curling white moustache and long white beard, and the oldest, yet most dazzling, diamond-sharp eyes you have even seen.

"Father Chri–" you begin before the flustered face peering up at you shushes you into silence.

"Now's not the time for introductions," he says. He is clearly old, but his expression is also one of the most powerful you have ever seen. "I've been captured by Krampus, the Christmas Devil," he explains, "and it looks like you're my only chance of getting out of here. My hands are tied, which is why I've been unable to free myself. You must get word to Jingle. He'll know what to do."

Turn to **380**.

145

You are horribly exposed on top of the glacier and the freezing weather exacts a terrible toll from your already frozen body.

(Deduct 2 *Endurance* points, 1 *Agility* point, and 1 *Combat* point.)

If you are still alive, now turn to **185**.

146

(Cross off one use of the *Naughty or Nice* special ability.)

"What's all this noise, wife?" comes a grunt from the back of the cave, and you realise for the first time that there is someone else here. "Is supper ready yet?"

"It will be, husband, once I've chucked this little blighter in the pot."

And then a repulsively ugly giant lumbers into view, scratching his backside with one hand, while picking at a boil on his nose with the other. It is Gryla's lazy husband, Leppaludi.

"Out of the way, woman," the giant rumbles, "I'll deal with this."

Picking up a meat-tenderising mallet, Leppaludi advances on your position.

If you now want to bring *The Pen is Mightier* special ability to bear, turn to **166**. If not, turn to **186**.

147

The gingerbread men turn their jelly sweet noses up at your offering, but it's too late to try to retrieve the food now.

Cross the item off your Adventure Sheet, as well as 1 Meal, and then turn to **419**.

148

The door to the south-east tower is hung with a Christmas wreath. Opening the door, beyond it you find a spiral stone staircase, which leads you up to a magnificent banqueting hall, hung with fine tapestries and bedecked with garlands of evergreens. There is even a great yule log blazing in the hearth driving the cold from the stone walls and floor of the chamber.

Overlooked by a stained glass window depicting four birds singing in the branches of a tree, a long table has been laid with a sumptuous feast, its centrepiece is a platter bearing a boar's head, festooned with holly, and a rosy red apple trapped between its teeth.

As well as there being fine food to eat – from frumenty and Christmas pie, to marchpane and Twelfth cake – there is also mulled cider to drink.

Do you want to sit down at the table and have something to eat (turn to **128**), do you want to pour yourself a drink (turn to **109**), or would you prefer not to eat or drink anything, and simply exit the tower again (turn to **381**)?

149

The red light in the robot's eye-visor dims, its sparking joints seize up, and the arcs of tamed lightning leaping between its antennae die. It looks like the robot has suffered some catastrophic malfunction, or perhaps it has just drained its batteries and run out of juice.

Turn to **390**.

150

You have been duped. It was no young woman asking to be let in from the cold, but a demonic servant of the one you have been pursuing, sent by your quarry to stop you before you can get any further. (In this battle, the succubus has the initiative.)

SUCCUBUS	COMBAT 7	ENDURANCE 7

If you manage to reduce the Succubus's *Endurance* score to 2 points or fewer, or after 4 Combat Rounds, whichever is sooner, turn to **180**.

151

You scramble onto the top of the box, and sit there, hoping that you are heavy enough to keep it closed, as the tinkling musical box counts down to the moment of release:

Half a pound of tuppenny rice,
Half a pound of treacle,
That's the way the money goes,
Pop goes the weasel!

At "Pop!" you are launched across the room by the force of the Jack-in-the-Box springing open. You slam into a wall and land in a heap on the floor.

Roll one die and lose this many *Endurance* points; if you roll a 1, deduct 2 *Endurance* points. (Alternatively, pick a card and deduct its face value from your *Endurance* score, unless it is 7 or above, or a picture card, in which case deduct 6 points from your *Endurance* score.)

If you lose 5 *Endurance* points or more, also deduct 1 *Agility* point and 1 *Combat* point.

If you are still alive, turn to **171**.

152

"Please!" the frozen creature begs. "I have an important message for you."

If you now want to open the window and let him in, turn to **112**. If you want to stand firm and not let the hobgoblin in, turn to **132**.

153

The carving knife still in hand, you plunge it straight through the turkey's breast and the animated fowl goes limp, dropping onto the table with a crash and sending sprouts cascading from their overloaded bowls.

Cross off one use of *The Pen is Mightier* special ability and turn to **214**.

154

The dimensions of the throne room seem to diminish somewhat, as you suddenly return to your normal size.

Clapping eyes on you, her frozen majesty screams, "How dare you enter the throne room of your queen uninvited!"

The elemental being becomes like a blizzard and flies the length of the throne room, as if borne on the wings of Boreas, the North Wind.

You have earned the enmity of the cold-hearted Snow Queen, for trespassing within her chamber, and now she will not be satisfied until you have paid for your crime with your life!

If you want to use *The Pen is Mightier* special ability, and you still can, turn to **9**. If not, turn to **273**.

155

Roll one die (or pick a card). If the number rolled is odd (or the card is red), turn to **195**. If the number rolled is even (or the card is black), turn to **175**.

156

You push the brass button to the left, and are immediately flung into the sky and dragged along in the wake of the sleigh's desperate flight.

You whirl through the sky, as if carried at the heart of a swirling vortex. It's like you're walking in the air! But even though you have no idea where you are going, the box seems to have a destination in mind, for it is not long before you catch sight of the sleigh again, through the blizzard. You are catching up with it!

Just when you think the snowstorm is going to deposit you in the back of the sleigh itself, you start to drop towards the ground, the power of the box seemingly spent, at least for the time being.

You land unceremoniously in a deep drift. Climbing out of it, and brushing the snow from your dressing-gown, and take in your surroundings.

You are in the depths of a forest. Snow covers the ground and the trees, and continues to fall from the sky, muffling all sound apart from the crunch of the stuff under your feet. What you wouldn't do for a pair of snow boots right now!

If you have the code word *Kosy* recorded on your Adventure Sheet, turn to **364**. If not, turn to **384**.

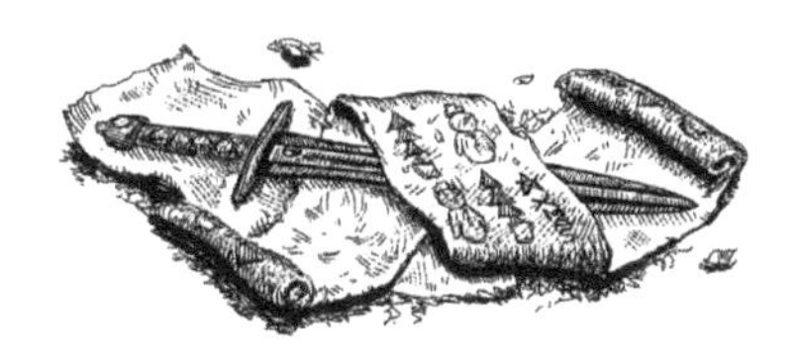

157

In a panic, you turn tail and run. But the cat is far nimbler and faster than you. With an almighty leap, the animal lands on your back, knocking you to the ground, its sharp claws ripping through your clothes and tearing the skin beneath.

Lose 2 *Endurance* points and, if you are still alive, turn to **137**.

158

Eventually the table is laid for the feast and the trolls are gathered around, their chops slavering as they peer into their empty bowls.

"Don't worry, my lads," Mama Gryla says, "supper's almost ready. I just need to add the final ingredient to the stew. Come on, Door-slammer, get that cage open, will you?"

Now's your chance to make a break for freedom, but as the troll in charge of the keys unlocks the cage, the giantess joins him, and yanks you out before you have a chance to run for it.

Not knowing what else to do, in your desperation to be free, you bite the hand holding you.

The giantess gives a cry of surprise and pain and drops you on the floor of the cave. (Deduct 2 *Endurance* points.)

"Why, you little blighter!" she snarls. "Bite me, would ya?"

Snatching up a cleaver as big as a forester's axe, she turns on you.

"I'll butcher you like the dog you are!" she roars.

How will you respond to such threatening behaviour? Will you:

Use *The Pen is Mightier* special ability? Turn to **96**.

Use your *Naughty or Nice* special ability? Turn to **146**.

Prepare to defend yourself? Turn to **116**.

159

Entering the sitting room, you quietly close the door behind you again. Everything appears to be normal: the Christmas cards are arrayed on shelves and windowsills; the stockings are hung in front of the fireplace; and a decorated fir tree stands in one corner, with presents piled beneath it.

The twinkling of the lights adorning the Christmas tree are just enough to see by, and you can make out the door at the other end of the room, which leads into the kitchen.

Will you:

Take a closer look at the Christmas cards?	Turn to **189**.
Take a closer look at the stockings to see if he's been already?	Turn to **219**.
Take a look at the Christmas tree?	Turn to **395**.

160

Despite your best efforts, as you try to evade the Snapdragon, you sustain several injuries.

Roll one die and deduct this many *Endurance* points. (Alternatively, pick a card and deduct its face value from your *Endurance* score, unless it is 7 or above or a picture card, in which case deduct 6 points from your *Endurance* score.)

If you are still alive, turn to **190**.

161

The sideboard is loaded with all manner of treats – from bowls of bonbons and candied orange peel, to platters of dates and walnuts – ready for Christmas Day.

Do you want to help yourself to some of the treats (turn to **8**), or would you prefer to see what's been laid out on the dining table (turn to **104**)?

162

Avoiding the main entrance, you make your way round to the side of the building and, easing open the large wooden door, enter the reindeer stables.

Inside, there are a number of stalls – eight altogether – and on the gate of each is a name plaque, painted in red, white and green. The one closest to you reads 'Comet'.

It is warm in the stables, and the air is thick with the smell of manure, mouldering straw, and the animals themselves. However, your arrival has clearly unsettled the beasts, as they start to snort and stamp the floor in agitation. But then, all things considered, it's hardly surprising they're on edge.

If you have some Carrots, turn to **191**. If not, turn to **211**.

163

With the monster gone, you make it to the far shore of the lake at last.

Turn to **446**.

164

Reverently taking the Silver Sword from you, the blacksmith shuffles from the forge into a backroom, and moments later you hear the creaking of a whetstone being turned on a peddled wooden frame, as he sets to work sharpening the blade.

While you sit by the fire, starting to feel warm and snug, there comes a knock at the door. Glancing towards the door to the backroom, you see no sign of movement; the blacksmith can't have heard the knocking over the noise of the whetstone.

The knock comes again, this time accompanied by an anxious female voice: "Please let me in, I'm freezing out here!"

If you want to open the door and let the poor woman in, turn to **233**. If you would prefer to stay where you are and hope that the blacksmith returns soon, turn to **193**.

165

Your fall is broken by the hard flagstones that cover the floor of the factory. Ouch!

Roll one die and add 2. Deduct this many *Endurance* points. (Alternatively, pick a card and deduct its face value from your *Endurance* score, unless it is 9 or above, or a picture card, in which case deduct 8 points from your *Endurance* score.)

If you have lost a total of 5 *Endurance* points or more, you must also deduct 1 point from your *Agility* score, and if you have lost a total of 7 *Endurance* points or more, also deduct 1 point from your *Combat* score.

If you are still alive, turn to **121**.

166

"You'll deal with this, will you, you lazy, good-for-nothing oaf?" screams his wife.

"Who are you calling a lazy good-for-nothing, you ugly harridan?" bellows the giant.

"Oh, I'm ugly now, am I?" shrieks Gryla.

"No, you've always been ugly," Leppaludi shouts back. "Now let me deal with this human bean for you! Know your place and stay in the kitchen!"

"My place?" roars the giantess, and starts thumping her husband.

"Hit me, would you?" snarls Leppaludi. "Why, I'll knock you into the middle of next week!"

Before you know it, the two giants are battering each other, and no longer paying any attention to you.

Cross off one use of *The Pen is Mightier* special ability and turn to **216**.

167

Although the Golem's crashing footfall sends plates and bowls tumbling from shelves to smash on the hard kitchen floor, you manage to stay on your feet.

Turn to **264**.

168

You hurtle through the gatehouse, as a portcullis of ice comes crashing down behind you, and over the ice bridge, just before its supporting arches give way, and it falls into the crevasse surrounding the castle.

Leaving the ruins of the Snow Queen's castle behind, you set off north again.

Turn to **244**.

169

As you battle the Christmas Devil, remember that you may add 2 bonus points when calculating your *Combat Rating*, and any successful hit you deliver with the sword will cause 1 additional point of damage.

Now turn to **328**.

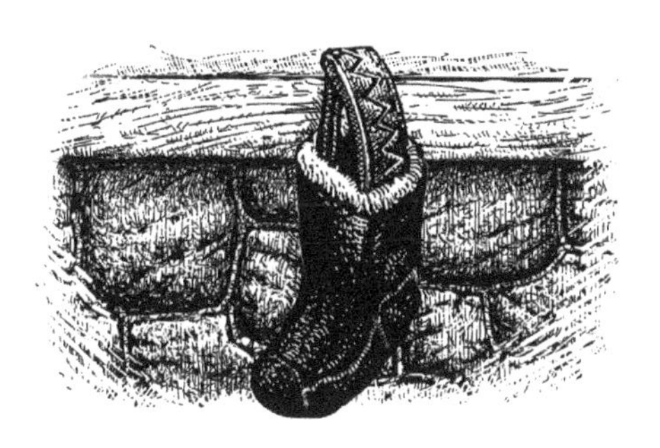

170

With the castle walls crashing down about your ears, you sprint for safety, hoping you can get out before the entire place collapses.

As you are crossing the courtyard, you hear a furious barking and see Venceslav coming towards you, riding a sled being pulled by a team of huskies.

"I found these fine fellows in the castle kennels," the deposed king tells you as the sled skids to a halt beside you. "Quick, jump on and then we'll be away from here! After all, I couldn't leave you behind, not after you freed me."

Not needing to be told twice, you jump onto the back of the sled, and with a shout of "Yaah!" and a crack of his whip, Venceslav sets the dogs running again.

They race through the crumbling gatehouse, the sled bouncing over the ice bridge, and safely to the other side, just moments before its supporting arches give way and it crashes down into the crevasse that surrounds the castle.

You are safe! That is, until the cold moon emerges from behind a shroud of cloud.

Venceslav gives a cry of pain and doubles up, his body contorting into agonised shapes. As you look on in horror, he starts to change. His body rapidly swells in size, bursting out of his clothes, revealing a shaggy white pelt beneath. His face elongates, with a horrible cracking sound – like bones breaking – as it becomes an ursine muzzle, while his hands transform into huge black-padded paws, embedded with lethal claws as long and as sharp as knives.

You are no longer sharing the sled with a crownless king but a furious polar bear. The huskies howl in fear and panic, dragging the sled down a bumpy slope, and you and the transformed Venceslav tumble from it into the snow.

Bellowing like the brute beast he now is, with a murderous bloodlust burning in his eyes, the Venceslav-bear goes for you.

If you want to use *The Pen is Mightier* special ability now, and you still can, turn to **139**. If not, turn to **480**.

171

Looming over you is a demented jester-like character, with an over-large smile splitting its porcelain face. The jester has stiletto-blades for fingers, and below its waist there is nothing but a shrouded spring.

A horrible, high-pitched giggle, running on repeat, comes from somewhere inside its chest, rather than its insanely leering mouth, as the Jack-in-a-Box lurches for you.

If you want to employ *The Pen is Mightier* special ability, turn to **209**. If not, turn to **101**.

As you flick through the pages of the book, it falls open at where a bookmark has been placed. Opposite a grotesque woodcut of a grinning demon, carrying a basket on its back, is the entry that describes Krampus, the Christmas Devil.

Krampus, The Christmas Devil

It is easy to forget that while Santa Claus delivers gifts to well-behaved little boys and girls during the festive period, bad little boys and girls face punishment from Krampus, the Christmas Devil.

But in the wild heartlands of Europe such legends are not so easily forgotten, and on the night of the Fifth of December, isolated communities honour the demonic anti-Santa who accompanies St. Nicholas during the Christmas season, by celebrating Krampusnacht.

The clanking of rusty chains and the clanging of cow bells warn of his approach. He is immediately identifiable, since he has two curling horns protruding from his head, but he also has one clawed foot and one goat's hoof. He wields a birch whip, which he uses to punish naughty children, and carries a basket on his back, into which he places those appalling urchins destined for the fiery pits of Hell.

The name Krampus itself originates from the Old High German word *krampen,* meaning 'claw'.

According to the entry in the book of folklore, Krampus's night is the Fifth of December and not Christmas Eve. For the devil to be out and about this night, something must have gone very wrong indeed!

Hearing a tapping at the window, you look up with a start to see a curious figure peering in from outside. He looks like a hobgoblin, his frozen hair sticking out in jagged points, and with icicles hanging from the end of his long, pointed nose.

Krampus

He looks absolutely frozen, his features pinched and blue from the cold. In fact, you could almost believe he was made entirely from ice, if it wasn't for his penetrating sapphire stare.

Where his tapping finger touches, feathers of frost spread across the window panes.

"Let me in!" pleads the curious creatures. "I'm so cold."

If you want to open the window so that the hobgoblin can enter the cottage, turn to **112**. If not, turn to **152**.

173

There isn't time to think as the robot fires its ray guns, only to react!

Take an Agility test. If you pass the test, turn to **29**, but if you fail the test, turn to **99**.

174

Now you know how the mouse feels in a game of cat and mouse, only this time it's the rodent that has the upper hand! (In this battle, the Rat has the initiative.)

RAT	COMBAT 8	ENDURANCE 8

If you kill the rat, turn to **204**.

175

Although momentum sends you flying some distance from the sleigh, you are fortunate enough to land in a deep snowdrift, which saves you from suffering any injuries.

Turn to **215**.

176

Taking a handful of the fruit and nuts from your pocket, you cast them onto the floor, and wait to see how the gingerbread men will react.

Roll one die (or pick a card). If the number rolled is odd (or the card is red), turn to **196**. If the number rolled is even (or the card is black), turn to **147**.

177

Taking off one of your slippers, you throw it at the cat. In response, the animal hisses, and then pounces. The feline catches your arm with an outstretched paw, its sharp claws drawing blood.

Lose 2 *Endurance* points and, if you are still alive, turn to **137**.

178

You fly through the air to land on a pile of presents, which breaks your fall.

Lose 2 *Endurance* points and, if you are still alive, turn to **121**.

179

The robot moves towards you on roller-feet, and tries to grab you with its snapping pincers. (Which one of you has the initiative will depend on how you got to this point.)

ROBOT	COMBAT 8	ENDURANCE 8

Thanks to its armoured shell, you must reduce any damage you manage to do the robot by 1 point.

If you overcome the battery-powered automaton, turn to **390**.

180

And then the blacksmith is there by your side, with a pair of red-hot tongs in his rough, callused hands. Pinching the demon's nose between the scalding pincers, he drags the screaming succubus back towards the door.

As he hauls her over the threshold, she suddenly sheds her clothes, and unfurls wings as broad and black as a dragon's. Escaping the blacksmith's hold at last, she takes to the air, still howling in pain as she flies away into the night.

The demon banished, the blacksmith returns your sword to you.

(Record the code word *Kruel* on your Adventure Sheet, and make a note that when you use the Silver Sword in battle, from now on you may add 2 points to your *Combat Rating*.)

Now turn to **310**.

181

You have conquered Krampus! The Christmas Devil has been defeated!

If you have the code word *Kringle* recorded on your Adventure Sheet turn to **347**. If not, turn to **269**.

182

There's no escaping the tentacles! If you carry on like this, they will fracture the frozen lake so drastically that you will be plunged into its gelid depths before you can get away from the grasping arms.

If you want to use *The Pen is Mightier* special ability, and you still can, turn to **202**. If not, make a note that you have the initiative in the battle to come and turn to **222**.

183

You have no choice but to fight the undead Christmas dinner! (In this battle, you have the initiative.)

ROAST TURKEY	COMBAT 6	ENDURANCE 5

If you win the fight, turn to **214**.

184

You take in the swags of tinsel, the fringed gold lamé, the endless links of paper-chains, and the tiny reindeer and elves wearing Santa hats that have been hung from every available light fitting and picture frame.

But then your brows crease in confusion as you lay eyes on something that you don't remember being put up when the room was being decorated. It looks like a string of tiny tinsel-wrapped skulls, as if someone has repurposed the Hallowe'en decorations in time for Christmas.

Turn to **206**.

185

Struggling over the fissured surface of the glacier, you make your way through the mountains until the ground underfoot starts to slope downwards, and you find yourself looking out across a vast ice-sheet. And there, not half a league away, you see the flickering of candle-light coming from the windows of a vast structure of stone and wood. It must be Santa's workshop!

Turn to **100**.

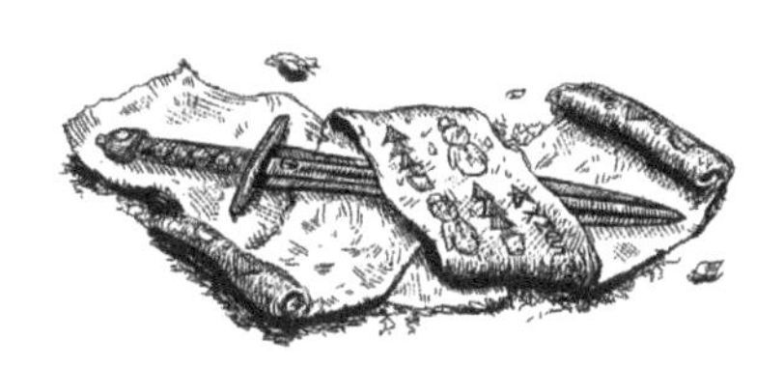

186

"No," Gryla tells her husband sternly, "we'll deal with this nuisance together!"

You must fight the giants at the same time, and in this battle, they have the initiative.

	COMBAT	ENDURANCE
LEPPALUDI	9	12
GRYLA	8	10

If you somehow manage to defeat the monstrous couple, turn to turn to **216**.

187

As you flee from the courtyard, a chunk of ice as big as a cart dislodges from the battlements and comes crashing down in front of you. It explodes into a million pieces on contact with the frozen ground and you are struck by the bombardment.

Roll one die and lose this many *Endurance* points; if you roll a 1, deduct 2 *Endurance* points. (Alternatively, pick a card and deduct its face value from your *Endurance* score, unless it is 7 or above, or a picture card, in which case deduct 6 points from your *Endurance* score.)

If you lose 5 *Endurance* points or more, also deduct 1 *Agility* point and 1 *Combat* point.

If you are still alive, you don't have time to treat your injuries, you just have to get out of the castle as quickly as you can – turn to **168**.

188

The pan flies past the hobgoblin's head and hits the windowsill, splashing the curtains with steaming claret.

Turn to **238**.

189

The cards are just what you would expect, bearing images of robins, Christmas trees, and quaint Dickensian village scenes featuring horse-drawn carriages in the snow. The flickering of the fairy lights, and the dull glow of the dying embers in the hearth, creates the illusion that the robins and red-liveried postmen are moving.

But as you scrutinize the cards, out of the corner of your eye, you are sure you see something darting through a crowd scene.

Do you want to:

Take a closer look at the card in question?	Turn to **49**.
Move on to take a closer look at the fireplace?	Turn to **219**.
Take a look at the tree, standing in the corner of the room?	Turn to **395**.

190

Once past the Snapdragon, you wonder what other challenges you will have to face as you run the Gauntlet of Games. You do not have to wait long to find out.

You hear a heavy grinding sound come from all around you, and the walls start to close in. If you do not reach the door at the other end, and fast, you will at best be trapped in here, and at worst killed – crushed to death by the contracting corridor!

If you want to call upon your *Naughty or Nice* special ability now, and you still can, turn to **240**. If not, turn to **260**.

191

You decide that the best way to settle Santa's reindeer would be to give them some fresh vegetables, and this you do, feeding each of them a carrot in turn. Their anxious snorting and stamping is replaced by the crunching of carrots and a contented cervine grunting. Comet is particularly appreciative.

(Record the code word *Komet* on your Adventure Sheet.)

With the reindeer unworried by your presence within the stable now, you set about exploring. It is not long before you stumble upon a candle lying in a pile of straw. (If you want to take it, add the Candle to the Equipment Box on your adventure sheet.)

At the far end of the shed is a door, which you imagine must lead to the main workshop complex. So fixated are you on the door, you do not notice the trapdoor, hidden beneath a scattering of straw, halfway along the length of the stable.

But you notice it when you step on it, and it gives way under your weight!

Turn to **275**.

192

You suddenly shrink down to the size of a GI Joe and the robot loses target-lock. This doesn't stop it unleashing a barrage of energy blasts at your last known position, but by then you are already moving.

The robot is actually guarding another door. As the mechanical menace's weapons blast holes in the floorboards, you dart past it unseen, and slip under the door before you return to your original size.

Turn to **492**.

193

"Please let me in," the woman pleads. But as you remain stoically in your seat by the fire, her tone becomes sharper. "Curse you then. You'll never make it beyond the ice caves anyway!"

(Record the code word *Kursed* on your Adventure Sheet.)

"Who's there?" demands the blacksmith, startling you. You hadn't realised he had returned to the forge.

Turn to **252**.

194

(Cross off one use of the special ability.)

As the Golem lumbers towards you, it steps on a rolling pin that has ended up on the floor in all the confusion. The offending foot shoots out from under it and, losing its balance, the cookie colossus topples backwards.

The old saying goes, 'The bigger they are, the harder they fall,' and this is certainly true of the Gingerbread Golem. What is more, the monster actually ends up with its head in the kitchen's large and fiery furnace of an oven.

Making the most of the opportunity, you make a break for it.

Turn to **300**.

195

Your body slams into the ground and you lie there, stunned. It feels like every part of you is hurting.

Roll one die and add 1. Deduct this many *Endurance* points. (Alternatively, pick a card and deduct its face value from your *Endurance* score, unless it is 8 or above or a picture card, in which case deduct 7 points from your *Endurance* score.)

If you lose 4 *Endurance* points or more, also deduct 1 *Combat* point and 1 *Agility* point.

Now turn to **215**.

196

Your plan works! As you scatter your offerings before them, the gingerbread men stop to pick them up and pop them into their tiny cake-holes. They even start fighting among themselves for the tastiest titbits!

With the kitchen's guardians distracted in this way, you are able to creep past them.

Cross off 1 Meal and turn to **300**.

197

Giving voice to a horrible yowling howl, the big cat leaps for you from the top of the tree stump. Do you want to:

Run away? Turn to **157**.

Defend yourself? Turn to **77**.

Use your *Naughty or Nice* special ability? Turn to **423**.

198

Turning to the back of the book, you find the entry for the sinister Yule Cat.

The Yule Cat

The Yule Cat - or *Jólakötturinn* - is a terrible carnivorous monster that stalks the winter wilderness, searching for prey. If you encounter it, it will devour you unless you make it an offering of new clothing - a wool sweater, socks, or something similar. But be warned, the demon cat will know if you are trying to trick it by offering it an old item of clothing!

Turn to **172**.

199

And then all hell breaks loose within the cave.

The trolls tumble over each other in an attempt to stop you getting away. As they make their clumsy grabs for you, you do all you can to evade them and reach the door, shoving them out of the way, tripping them up, and throwing things at them that you grab from the table.

You need to work out how many of the trolls you manage to put out of action as you race around the cave.

Take an Agility test, a Combat test, and an Endurance test. Then roll one die (or pick a card). You may also choose to spend one use of *The Pen is Mightier* special ability and one use of the *Naughty or Nice* special ability. Having done all of these things, consult the table below to see how many points you have scored.

Passed the *Agility* test	+1 point
Passed the *Combat* test	+1 point
Passed the *Endurance* test	+2 points
The number rolled is even (or the card is black)	+1 point
Used *The Pen is Mightier* special ability	+2 points
Used the *Naughty or Nice* special ability	+2 points
You have a Blacksmith's Axe	+1 point
You have a Silver Sword	+2 points

Once you have calculated your points total, turn to **239**.

200

You set off around the edge of the lake, not wanting to remain out in the open any longer than is really necessary. But then the wind starts to rise again and you are forced to fight for every step as you advance through the biting blizzard.

Between the gusting flurries of snow, you see something through the whiteout; something that is only a little darker than the snow shrouding it. And then you see the red stains besmirching the snow.

As you draw closer still, there is a temporary respite from the gale, as the wind drops, and the macabre scene is revealed.

Lying in the snow is the body of what is clearly a dead reindeer. And picking at the carcass are a pair of large, white wolves.

There is no indication that the wolves have seen you, and you are down wind of them, so they can't have picked up your scent either.

What do you want to do? Will you:

Try to sneak past the feeding wolves?	Turn to **130**.
Take to your heels and run as fast as you can?	Turn to **449**.
Attack the wolves, before they can attack you?	Turn to **19**.
Attempt to cross the frozen lake instead?	Turn to **370**.

201

"We have a winner!" announces the woman, in a disinterested tone, and the crowd that has gathered to watch offers up a polite round of applause.

The owner of the stall takes the bow back from you and gives you a bottle of eggnog.

The Bottle of Eggnog contains three measures, and each measure will restore 3 *Endurance* points. However, if you drink more than one measure in one go, you must also reduce your *Combat* score by 1 point for every measure over the initial one that you drink, until after your next battle. (For example, if you drank two measures in one go, you would have to temporarily reduce your *Combat* score by 1 point, but if you emptied the bottle in one go, you would have to reduce your *Combat* score by 2 points.)

Happy with your prize, you set off again through the fair.

Record the Bottle of Eggnog on your Adventure Sheet and turn to **241**.

202

Suddenly, for no obvious reason, the squid breaks off its attack and returns to the lightless depths of the gelid lake.

Turn to **163**.

203

You must fight the slavering beasts at the same time! (Who has the initiative depends on the events that have conspired to bring you to this point.)

	COMBAT	ENDURANCE
First WHITE WOLF	7	7
Second WHITE WOLF	6	6

If you defeat both predators, turn to **83**.

204

With the rat out of the way, you make your escape through the crack in the cave wall. Following the fissure, you soon find yourself back outside, in the snow and the darkness of the Christmas night.

Returning the knob on top of the box to its central position, you return to your normal size, and set off once more, moving ever northwards.

Turn to **473**.

13

wearisome, and so you decide
up against a tree stump. (Now
Meal, if you would like to.)

here that you become aware of
ing of paws on snow. Possessed
mething is creeping up on you,
d spin round, as a huge black
h an outstretched paw, claws

fiercely glowing orange eyes,
r of coal, and it is as big as a

sy written on your Adventure
o **197**.

14

hasn't done anything to lessen
as increased it! – and you finish
ou keep a weather eye on the
usages start wriggling. (Gain 4

ou may take the Carving Knife
venture Sheet and make a note
you may add 1 point to your

hat your adventure is not over
m through a door on the far
crets are hiding within Santa's

205

You can see that the north-east tower of the castle is different from the rest straightaway, since its walls are covered with knotty growths of holly and ivy. There is no door in the bottom of the tower, just a window high up at the top. The only way to reach it would be to climb the flourishing evergreens.

If you want to attempt to climb up to the window, turn to **225**. If you think such an ascent would be too risky, turn to **381**.

206

A tinsel garland suddenly slips free of the mirror frame and hangs loose. Reaching out to push it back into place, you are startled when the tinsel jerks out of the way. And then, in the next heartbeat, it lashes out like a whip, wrapping itself around your neck. You gasp in surprise as more of the strings of decorations shake themselves loose and, snake-like, bind you in their ever-tightening coils.

You start to panic as the tinsel tightens about your neck, and soon you are gasping for breath!

If you want to call on your *The Pen is Mightier* special ability, turn to **226**. If you want to use your *Naughty or Nice* special ability, turn to **266**. But if you don't want to use either of these abilities now, turn to **246**.

207

With the castle walls crashing down about your ears, you sprint for safety, hoping to get out before the entire place collapses.

Take an Agility test. If you pass the test, turn to **168**. If you fail the test, turn to **187**.

208

You turn and run from the cookie colossus, but the Gingerbread Golem's reach is long. Before you can get away, the monstrous confection reaches down, seizing you in a huge half-baked hand, and starts to squeeze.

Take an Endurance test. If you pass the test, turn to **243**, but if you fail the test, turn to **223**.

209

Just as you think your time is up, suddenly, and completely unexpectedly, the spring recoils back into the box, dragging the startled-looking jester with it. The lid of the Jack-in-the-Box slams shut once more, and you are free to go.

Turn to **242**.

210

As you sit by the fire, you and the blacksmith talk some more.

"Far to the north," he says, "within the shadow in the mountains, there lies a castle. You might seek shelter there, but I doubt that's where Krampus has gone. It sounds to me like you'll need to search beyond the mountains if you're to find him."

You know that if you remain cocooned within the cosy warmth of the forge for too long, the less likely you are to want to leave it again.

But then there comes a knock at the door.

"Who's there?" demands the blacksmith, getting to his feet.

Turn to **252**.

Trudging through the snow i
to rest for a moment, proppe
would be a good time to eat a

But it is while you are resting
the almost imperceptible pad
of the unnerving feeling that s
you scramble to your feet a
cat makes a grab for you w
unsheathed.

It looks like a wild cat, with
except that its fur is the colo
fully-grown panther.

If you have the code word *K*
Sheet, turn to **237**. If not, turn

Your encounter with the turke
your appetite – if anything, it
what you started, although y
pigs-in-blankets, in case the s
Endurance points.)

If you are without a weapon,
with you; record it on your A
that when you use it in battl
Combat Rating.

Once you are done, knowing
yet, you leave the dining ro
side, wondering what other s
workshop.

Turn to **492**.

215

As you pick yourself up, brushing the snow from your dressing-gown, you hear the diabolical monster bellowing at the reindeer, urging them to get up. Before you can do anything to stop it, the creature climbs back into the driver's seat.

One crack of the devil's whip sends the reindeer galloping into the sky again, dragging the battered sleigh after them, and leaving you all alone in the snowy wilderness, with no idea of where you are or how to get home.

You are in the depths of a forest. Snow covers the ground and the trees, and continues to fall from the sky, muffling all sound apart from the crunch of the stuff under your feet. What you wouldn't do for a pair of snow boots right now!

If you have the code word *Kosy* recorded on your Adventure Sheet, turn to **364**. If not, turn to **384**.

216

You have escaped the murderous giantess Gryla! (Record the code word *Kretinous* on your Adventure Sheet.)

If you have the code word *Krowded* already recorded on your Adventure Sheet, turn to **56**. If not, turn to **236**.

217

You suspect that the only thing worth offering the gingerbread men would be something nice to eat? But what foodstuffs do you have to offer them?

Some boiled sweets?	Turn to **196**.
Some dried fruit and nuts?	Turn to **176**.
Some carrots?	Turn to **147**.
Some savoury snacks?	Turn to **87**.
Some gingerbread?	Turn to **127**.

218

Turning on your heel you run for the door, hoping to escape the cottage and perhaps trap your attacker inside before the hobgoblin can catch you.

Take an Agility test. If you pass the test, turn to **323**, but if you fail the test, turn to **238**.

219

The mantelpiece is wound with tinsel and decked with swatches of fir, while the stockings hang from hooks in front of the fire. Running your fingertips over the wood of the mantelpiece you feel the tracks of something scratched into its surface. Peering closer, by the orange glow of the dying embers, you make out four words gouged into the wood, as if by a sharp claw.

YOU'D BETTER BE GOOD!

That wasn't there when you went to bed!

The sight of the sinister message sets your heart racing again. As you are wondering who could have carved those words into the wood, you realise that the stockings are bulging. Someone has put something in them. However, the glass of sherry and plate of mince pies left out for Santa, as well as the carrots for his reindeer, are still on the little table by the fire.

It is then that you notice the sooty footprints on the rug in front of the hearth. One of them looks vaguely human, but the other was clearly left by a hoof!

You feel like you could do with some sherry yourself, to help settle your nerves.

Do you want to:

Drink the sherry?	Turn to **247**.
Take a look inside the stockings?	Turn to **277**.
Move on to take a look at the tree?	Turn to **395**.

220

There's no changing the course of the narrative now. This is how the story ends, with you battling Krampus the Christmas Devil!

In your moment of hesitation, the fiend strikes you with his birch-whip.

"Do you know what your chance is of winning, pray tell?
You'd get better odds on a snowflake in hell!"

(Lose 2 *Endurance* points.)

If you are still alive, continue your battle with the Christmas Devil, in which he now has the initiative, and if you are victorious in your battle with the anti-Santa, turn to **181**.

221

It's no good, you just can't get your eye in, and so you walk away from the archery stall empty-handed.

Turn to **241**.

205

You can see that the north-east tower of the castle is different from the rest straightaway, since its walls are covered with knotty growths of holly and ivy. There is no door in the bottom of the tower, just a window high up at the top. The only way to reach it would be to climb the flourishing evergreens.

If you want to attempt to climb up to the window, turn to **225**. If you think such an ascent would be too risky, turn to **381**.

206

A tinsel garland suddenly slips free of the mirror frame and hangs loose. Reaching out to push it back into place, you are startled when the tinsel jerks out of the way. And then, in the next heartbeat, it lashes out like a whip, wrapping itself around your neck. You gasp in surprise as more of the strings of decorations shake themselves loose and, snake-like, bind you in their ever-tightening coils.

You start to panic as the tinsel tightens about your neck, and soon you are gasping for breath!

If you want to call on your *The Pen is Mightier* special ability, turn to **226**. If you want to use your *Naughty or Nice* special ability, turn to **266**. But if you don't want to use either of these abilities now, turn to **246**.

207

With the castle walls crashing down about your ears, you sprint for safety, hoping to get out before the entire place collapses.

Take an Agility test. If you pass the test, turn to **168**. If you fail the test, turn to **187**.

208

You turn and run from the cookie colossus, but the Gingerbread Golem's reach is long. Before you can get away, the monstrous confection reaches down, seizing you in a huge half-baked hand, and starts to squeeze.

Take an Endurance test. If you pass the test, turn to **243**, but if you fail the test, turn to **223**.

209

Just as you think your time is up, suddenly, and completely unexpectedly, the spring recoils back into the box, dragging the startled-looking jester with it. The lid of the Jack-in-the-Box slams shut once more, and you are free to go.

Turn to **242**.

210

As you sit by the fire, you and the blacksmith talk some more.

"Far to the north," he says, "within the shadow in the mountains, there lies a castle. You might seek shelter there, but I doubt that's where Krampus has gone. It sounds to me like you'll need to search beyond the mountains if you're to find him."

You know that if you remain cocooned within the cosy warmth of the forge for too long, the less likely you are to want to leave it again.

But then there comes a knock at the door.

"Who's there?" demands the blacksmith, getting to his feet.

Turn to **252**.

211

The reindeer become more and more agitated by your presence, and start to upset each other, stamping their hooves and snorting in distress. And it is not long before you hear the grating of a door handle turning, and the creak of hinges.

Opening the gate to one of the stalls you dart through, and find yourself in what must be the only empty pen in the place.

Hearing the jangling of bells, cautiously peering out from your hiding place, you see a number of stunted figures enter the stable. From their brightly-coloured garb and pointed hats, at first you take them for Santa's little helpers – the elfin folk that populate the legends about Father Christmas. But then you catch sight of their hideous faces and spiteful leers, and you realise they look more like demonic imps, doubtless in the service of the Christmas Devil himself.

The imps are coming closer with every step, as they search the stable, trying to get to the bottom of what has upset the reindeer. It can only be a matter of time before they find you.

What do you want to do? Will you:

Use the *Naughty or Nice* special ability (if you still can)?	Turn to **231**.
Use *The Pen is Mightier* special ability (if you still can)?	Turn to **21**.
Take the initiative and attack the imps?	Turn to **251**.

212

The box might be your only way out of your dire predicament.

If you know what to do to go small, and you still want to use the box, do it now. If you don't know, or don't want to use the box after all, turn to **173**.

213

Trudging through the snow is wearisome, and so you decide to rest for a moment, propped up against a tree stump. (Now would be a good time to eat a Meal, if you would like to.)

But it is while you are resting there that you become aware of the almost imperceptible padding of paws on snow. Possessed of the unnerving feeling that something is creeping up on you, you scramble to your feet and spin round, as a huge black cat makes a grab for you with an outstretched paw, claws unsheathed.

It looks like a wild cat, with fiercely glowing orange eyes, except that its fur is the colour of coal, and it is as big as a fully-grown panther.

If you have the code word *Kosy* written on your Adventure Sheet, turn to **237**. If not, turn to **197**.

214

Your encounter with the turkey hasn't done anything to lessen your appetite – if anything, it has increased it! – and you finish what you started, although you keep a weather eye on the pigs-in-blankets, in case the sausages start wriggling. (Gain 4 *Endurance* points.)

If you are without a weapon, you may take the Carving Knife with you; record it on your Adventure Sheet and make a note that when you use it in battle, you may add 1 point to your *Combat Rating.*

Once you are done, knowing that your adventure is not over yet, you leave the dining room through a door on the far side, wondering what other secrets are hiding within Santa's workshop.

Turn to **492**.

222

Not even in your worst nightmares did you ever think you would have to battle a horror such as the Ice Squid! (Which of you has the initiative will depend upon the chain of events that have led you to this point.)

ICE SQUID	COMBAT 10	ENDURANCE 10

If you reduce the Ice Squid's *Endurance* score to zero, you have not killed the beast, you have merely done enough to discourage it from attacking you anymore and it sinks back into the depths of the arctic lake.

Turn to **163**.

223

Despite pushing against the crushing grip of the Golem with all the strength you can muster, it is not enough. Steadily the half-baked horror tightens its grip until you are no longer able to breathe, as it smothers you with a palm made of gingerbread dough.

Your adventure comes to an end, suffocated within the grasp of a gigantic gingerbread man. Oh, what sweet release!

The End

224

Your heart racing, you bring the battle to the animated ice guards. (You must fight them both at the same time, but in this battle you have the initiative.)

	COMBAT	ENDURANCE
First ICE GUARDIAN	7	8
Second ICE GUARDIAN	7	8

If you are wielding an axe, any successful hit you deliver with the heavy-bladed weapon will cause 1 additional point of damage, as it smashes away at their frozen forms.

If you manage to defeat the Ice Guardians, turn to **295**.

225

Taking hold of great handfuls of the ivy vines and the wooden branches of the holly, you commence your climb.

Take an Endurance test. If you pass the test, turn to **397**, but if you fail the test, turn to **245**.

226

(Cross off one use of *The Pen is Mightier* special ability.)

You manage to fight your way free of the dangling decorations, the serpentine swags tying themselves in knots as you escape their constricting coils.

Turn to **286**.

227

The Snow Queen's hold over this place broken, a violent shaking besets the foundations of the frozen fortress. Great blocks of masonry and ice come crashing down as the castle starts to collapse.

If you have the code word *Krowned* recorded on your Adventure Sheet, turn to **170**. If not, turn to **207**.

228

You find the entry you are looking for near the back of the book, and start to read.

Snow Sprites

People have carved figures from snow and ice for thousands of years, whilst also worshipping the elements in the hope of appeasing them. Over the centuries this intense belief has led to the creation of elemental spirits of winter. Some, such as Jack Frost, have gained a sentience and life of their own, whereas others wait deep under the ground, or frozen in glaciers, until the temperature drops, when they can inhabit snow sculptures. Those wise in the ways of elemental magic can bend these Snow Sprites to do their bidding. They are, however, particularly susceptible to heat, in any form.

Turn to **172**.

229

The Jack-in-the-Box is defeated!

As you pick your way past the broken over-sized toy, amidst the pieces of cloth and uncoiled spring, you spot something – it is a skeleton key!

(If you want to take it, add the Skeleton Key to the Equipment box on your Adventure Sheet.)

Whether you take the key with you or not, you leave the room through the far door, closing it firmly behind you.

Turn to **7**.

230

Your ears pop as you rocket towards the ground. And then, through the snowy darkness, the tips of trees come into view and you realise that the sleigh is on a collision course with a dense pine forest. You pull back hard on the reins, and the reindeer nose upwards, rising over the treetops, the runners of the sleigh skidding from the snow-decked branches before following them up into the air again.

Snarling like a savage animal, and having regained its balance, the strange cloaked figure goes for you.

Make a note that your opponent has the initiative in the battle to come, and record the code word *Krazy* on your Adventure Sheet before turning to **131**.

231

Only three imps entered the stable to begin with, but now they are joined by five more – and all of them are looking for you! It does not take them long to find you.

While you fight back as best you can, penned within the stall, the imps soon overpower you and take you captive.

Deduct 4 *Endurance* points, cross off one use of the *Naughty or Nice* special ability, and if you are still alive, turn to **452**.

232

Roll one die (or pick a card). If the number rolled is odd (or the card is red), turn to **165**. If the number rolled is even (or the card is black), turn to **178**.

233

Lifting the latch, you open the door to find a beautiful young woman standing there, a shawl pulled tight under her chin, and held in place by one ice-blue hand.

Roll one die (or pick a card). If the number rolled is odd (or the card is red), turn to **110**. If the number rolled is even (or the card is black), turn to **10**.

234

Your arms pinned to your sides, within the giantess's grasp, you can do nothing as she makes her way through the forest with great lumbering strides, until the ground starts to rise and becomes rocky underfoot. Through the trees you see a flickering light, coming from a small window at the entrance to a large cave. However, the entrance has been blocked up by a circular doorway that is twice as tall as you are.

Opening the door, the giantess stoops to pass through it. As she carries you inside, you cannot help but stare in amazement at the sight that greets you.

The cave has been furnished as if it's someone's home. There is a long table, dressers are pushed up against the walls, and you can see several bunk beds. At the back of the cave a large cauldron of water has been set to boil over a large fire, the smoke from which disappears up a chimney breast that has been built into the cave wall.

But most astonishing of all are the cave's inhabitants. It is full of curious, troll-like beings – you count thirteen in all.

"What have you got there, Mama Gryla?" asked one of the misshapen creatures.

"Supper!" replies the giantess.

Turn to **254**.

235

Down and down you fall, as the snowflakes whirl around you and the ground rushes up to meet you.

If you want to use your *Naughty or Nice* special ability, cross off one use and turn to **288**. If not, turn to **258**.

236

"What have you done?" shrieks one of the trolls, suddenly appearing from under the table.

"You're not getting out of here alive," growls another, striding towards you, swinging a cruel-looking meat-hook in one hand. "Did you know that?"

Turn to **199**.

237

The big cat hisses and spits at you, but it doesn't attack. While it considers you, with its head tilted to one side, as if trying to decide what to do with you, you decide to take control of the situation.

Will you:

Run away?	Turn to **157**.
Try to shoo the animal away?	Turn to **177**.
Attack the cat?	Turn to **77**.
Offer it something?	Turn to **305**.
Use your *Naughty or Nice* special ability?	Turn to **423**.

238

Before you can twist out of its reach, the creature grabs you by the wrist. You immediately feel a numbing chill seep into your bones that makes you gasp in shock.

Lose 1 *Endurance* point and 1 *Combat* point, and then turn to **268**.

239

The number of points you have scored is the number of trolls you have already knocked out, pushed out of the way, or tripped up as you frantically race around the cave. Any trolls already eliminated come from the bottom of the following list, but you will have to fight the rest of the Yule Lads! (In this battle, you have the initiative.)

	COMBAT	ENDURANCE
MEAT-HOOK	8	7
SHEEP-COTE CLOD	7	7
GULLY GAWK	7	6
STUBBY	5	5
SPOON-LICKER	6	5
POT-SCRAPER	7	8
BOWL-LICKER	7	8
DOOR-SLAMMER	8	7
SKYR-GOBBLER	7	6
SAUSAGE-SWIPER	7	7
WINDOW-PEEPER	6	7
DOORWAY-SNIFFER	6	6
CANDLE-STEALER	5	6

If you manage to do away with all of the Yule Lads, turn to **36**.

240

Clearly on this occasion the universe decides you have been nice, or at least nice enough to be given a second chance.

The grinding noise gives way to a cacophonous clanking sound, as something – maybe a drive shaft – snaps. Whatever the specific details of the malfunction, the serendipitous result is that the walls stop moving.

Cross off one use of the *Naughty or Nice* special ability and turn to **440**.

241

In the shadow of one of the bridge's stone arches, you see that someone has set up a Punch and Judy show. Standing beside the red-and-yellow-striped canvas booth is a little old man in a worn grey overcoat and wide-brimmed hat, with a thick white beard, and a red spotted kerchief tied about his neck.

The old man's dog, an Irish terrier, runs over to you and starts skipping around your feet.

Turn to **447**.

242

You make it to the far door and throw yourself through, slamming it shut again behind you. But your troubles are not over yet…

Turn to **7**.

243

Pushing with all your might against the Golem's crushing grip, in your desperation you manage to force the huge fingers apart. Free again, you drop onto a table, sending marzipan fruits flying in all directions.

Turn to **264**.

244

And so you come at last to the foot of a steep mountain pass, and the great tongue of ice that protrudes from it. The front face of the glacier rises like a cliff far above your head. And yet, if you are to proceed beyond the ice-rimed peaks, you are going to have to attempt to scale its frozen immensity.

If you have a Pair of Ice Picks, turn to **45**. If not, turn to **25**.

245

It is so cold, the wall is so icy, and you are so tired, is it any wonder that you suddenly lose your grip on the plants and fall from the tower?

Roll one die (or pick a card). If the number rolled is odd (or the card is red), turn to **285**. If the number rolled is even (or the card is black), turn to **265**.

246

Struggling to breathe, you fight for your life as the decorations try to truss you up like a Christmas turkey and strangle you! (In this battle, the decorations have the initiative.)

DEVILISH DECORATIONS	COMBAT 8	ENDURANCE 6

If you manage to get the better of the decorations before they get the better of you, turn to **286**.

247

You empty the glass in one gulp and immediately feel the fortified wine warming your body from the inside. It also has the desired effect of making you feel more relaxed again. (For the duration of the next fight you are involved in, you may add 1 point when calculating your *Combat Rating*.)

Your stomach rumbling – it is several hours since you last ate, after all – you quickly polish off the plate of mince pies too, and put the carrots in your pocket for later, just in case. (Gain 2 *Endurance* points and record the Carrots on your Adventure Sheet.)

Now do you want to take a look inside the stockings hanging by the fire (turn to **277**), or move on to look at the tree (turn to **395**)?

248

Heeding the old man's advice, you hurry over to the spot where the Christmas Devil now lies sprawled in the snow. And you were right to check on him; the mistletoe spear has become lodged in Krampus's shoulder, and not his heart! He has the luck of the Devil!

(Record the code word *Kritical* on your Adventure Sheet.)

At your approach, Krampus leaps to his feet, ready to finish you in single combat.

If you have the Ledger of Souls with you, you will have a number associated with it; turn to that section number now. If not, turn to **74**.

249

Because you are using the Silver Sword against the Christmas Devil, you may add 2 bonus points when calculating your *Combat Rating*.

Now turn to **328.**

250

You are about to leave when you are reminded of what Jingle the Elf told you, about Mrs Christmas's pantry being off the kitchens. If you don't free the Elves, who else will? You owe it to them to at least try to find the key to their prison.

Darting glances around you, through the clouds of steam filling the kitchen you suddenly catch sight of a door with a painted sign on it that reads, 'Home Sweet Home'.

You are sure this is what you are looking for. Keeping close to the wall, you dart across to the door and, opening it, sneak through, closing it quietly again behind you.

Hearing a muffled grunt from behind you, you spin round and are met by a shocking sight.

Bound to her rocking chair by heavy ropes is a plump lady, of indeterminate age, a pair of round spectacles perched on the end of her nose, and with a mob cap covering her grey curls. Her clothes are of red velvet, trimmed with white fur, and she is also wearing an apron.

But the sight of the one you are sure has imprisoned her here is even more shocking. It is quite clearly a humanoid figure, six feet tall, but made entirely of sweets – everything from liquorice and coconut ice, to candyfloss and fluffy marshmallows.

"How sweet!" the candy creature cries in a shrill voice. "Another plaything for the Candyman."

Pulling a red-hot poker from the grate of the little fire that warms Mrs Christmas's pantry, the sugary psychopath advances, saying, "What game shall we play today? Squeal Piggy Squeal?"

You are going to have to act fast if you are to save Mrs Christmas and yourself from the ministrations of the creepy Candyman.

If you want to use the *Naughty or Nice* special ability, and you still can, turn to **450**. If not, turn to **488**.

251

Leaping out from the stall, you take the imps by surprise, the creatures crying out in alarm as you attack. (In this battle, you have the initiative, and in the confines of the stable you may fight your opponents two at a time.)

	COMBAT	ENDURANCE
First IMP	6	6
Second IMP	5	5
Third IMP	6	5

If you win the fight, turn to **41**.

252

He pulls open the door. Standing there is a beautiful young woman, a shawl pulled tight under her chin, and held in place by one ice-blue hand.

Following the blacksmith's horrified gaze, as the woman takes a step over the threshold, you see that under her skirts, rather than feet, she has the cloven hooves of a goat.

"Begone, deceiver!" the blacksmith cries, grabbing a pair of red-hot iron tongs from the forge. Catching the demon's nose between the glowing pincers, he drags her, kicking and screaming, outside.

Suddenly shedding her clothes, she unfurls wings as broad and black as a dragon's and, escaping the blacksmith's hold, takes to the air, still howling in pain as she flies away into the night.

Record the code word *Kruel* on your Adventure Sheet and turn to **310**.

253

You are standing at the end of a long passageway. At the other end you can just make out another door.

You try the handle of the door through which you entered, but it is now firmly locked. The only way onwards is along the passageway, unless you happen to have a set of Lockpicks about your person.

If you do, and you want to use them now to unlock the door and return to the antechamber, from there choosing the door labelled 'TOYS' instead – turn to **432**.

If not, you have no choice but to advance along the passageway – turn to **279**.

254

You are thrown into a rusted iron cage beside the fire, and locked inside by one of the trolls, who carries a number of keys on a large iron ring.

"Get that fire nice and hot," the giantess instructs the trolls.

"Yes, Mama Gryla," they reply, and start throwing on more logs.

"We're having bean stew for supper!" Mama Gryla announces.

"What kind of bean?" asks one of her sons.

"Human bean, of course, Pot-Scraper!" the giantess grins.

Unless you want to become supper for the trolls and their giantess mother, you have to get out of both the cage and the cave, and fast! But how?

Will you:

Use the Box of Delights (if you have it)?	Turn to **311**.
Use a set of Lockpicks (if you have some)?	Turn to **371**.
Offer your captors a drink of Schnapps (if you have some)?	Turn to **391**.
Offer your captors some Carrots (if you have some)?	Turn to **451**.
Plead with the trolls to let you go?	Turn to **2**.

255

(Cross off one use of the *Naughty or Nice* special ability.)

Before you can reach the door, the pudding explodes. The blast throws you against the wall, and you rebound off it to land in a heap on the floor, as pieces of burning plum pudding rain down around you.

Roll one die and add 2, then divide the total by 2, rounding fractions up. Deduct this many *Endurance* points. (Alternatively, pick a card and deduct its face value from your *Endurance* score, unless it is 5 or above, or a picture card, in which case deduct 4 points from your *Endurance* score.)

If you are still alive, turn to **376**.

256

The freezing wind shows no sign of letting up and blows flurries of snowflakes into your face with every step you take.

If you are in possession of the Box of Delights, turn to **409**. If not, turn to **280**.

257

The spear goes wide of the mark, landing in the snow somewhere to the right of the Christmas Devil.

Your failure causes you to doubt your own abilities. (Lose 1 *Combat* point.)

If you have the Ledger of Souls with you, you will have a number associated with it; turn to that section number now. If not, turn to **74**.

258

Roll one die (or pick a card). If the number rolled is odd (or the card is red), turn to **318**. If the number rolled is even (or the card is black), turn to **288**.

259

It is no good – you are unable to maintain your balance as the wooden conveyor rattles under your feet, and as the belt suddenly turns ninety degrees to the left, you are thrown off on the bend. But where will you land?

If you want to tempt fate by using your *Naughty or Nice* special ability, and you can still do so, cross off one use and turn to **178**. If not, turn to **232**.

260

Once again you find yourself running to escape certain death!

Take an Endurance test. If you pass the test, turn to **440**, but if you fail the test, turn to **410**.

261

In your moment of desperation, an idea hits you like a blow to the back of the head. Pulling a hobby horse from a bucket by the door, you hurl it at the lantern hanging from the ceiling.

Just as you had hoped, the whirling wooden pole strikes the lantern, knocking it from its hook, and it falls onto the floor beside the advancing teddy bear. You watch, half in horror and half in delight, as the lantern shatters, dousing the malign animated monstrosity with burning oil.

The bear goes up in an instant. It flails about the room, setting fire to other stuffed toys as it does so, a high-pitched shriek rising from amidst the flames.

Making the most of the opportunity, you sprint the length of the room, past the burning bear.

Cross off one use of *The Pen is Mightier* special ability and turn to **242**.

262

You might feel like you are freezing, but you are still warm-blooded, while the keep of the castle is entirely made of ice. Just by being here, the heat given off by your body has raised the temperature in the antechamber by a fraction of a degree – but it is enough.

The join between an ornate gargoyle and the lintel above the double doors warms up enough to become water again, and the heavy ice carving comes crashing down on top of the guards, smashing them to smithereens.

Cross off one use of *The Pen is Mightier* special ability and turn to **295**.

263

You find the passage in the book, luridly illustrated with images of grinning imps – some with wings and some without – and start to read.

Imps

Imps are lesser demonic servants, often bound to the service of a witch or warlock, or a higher ranking devil. They are mischievous to the point of malevolence and have a little magic. In larger numbers they can prove to be very dangerous indeed.

Turn to **172**.

264

The giant gingerbread man seems intent on doing away with you, and you are fast running out of options!

If you want to use *The Pen is Mightier* special ability, turn to **194**. If not, turn to **282**.

265

Fortunately, you are not even halfway up the tower when you fall.

Roll one die and lose this many *Endurance* points; if you roll a 1, deduct 2 *Endurance* points. (Alternatively, pick a card and deduct its face value from your *Endurance* score, unless it is 7 or above, or a picture card, in which case deduct 6 points from your *Endurance* score.)

If you lose 5 *Endurance* points or more, also deduct 1 *Agility* point and 1 *Combat* point.

If you survive the fall, turn to **317**.

266

(Cross off one use of the *Naughty or Nice* special ability.)

As you struggle to free yourself, even more ribbons of tinsel and the loops of paper-chains descend upon you, tightening their hold.

If you now want to employ *The Pen is Mightier* special ability, turn to **226**. If not, turn to **246** and reduce your *Combat Rating* by 1 point for the duration of the next battle you have to fight.

267

If you want to get away from the advancing imps, then going swift would seem to be the order of the day.

If you know what to do to go swift, do it now. If you don't know, or you want to try something else, will you run away (turn to **434**), or bring the fight to the imps (turn to **463**)?

268

"You don't get away from Jack Frost that easily!" the hobgoblin snickers.

If you're not careful, Jack Frost will be nipping at more than just your nose! (In this battle, the hobgoblin has the initiative.)

JACK FROST	COMBAT 8	ENDURANCE 7

If Jack Frost wins a Combat Round, turn to **298** at once. If you manage to reduce the hobgoblin's *Endurance* score to 3 points or fewer, or after five Combat Rounds, whichever is sooner, turn to **323**.

269

A violent tremor passes through the top of the hill and the ground suddenly, and dramatically, splits open. An ever-widening fissure zigzags towards you, and you are struck by a gust of superheated air that rises from its infernal depths.

But it isn't you who is sent tumbling into the pit. With a final braying scream of frustration, rage and pain, it is the demon who is sent plummeting into the abyss, and all his hellish minions are dragged down with him.

Turn to **500.**

270

Suddenly, through the snowy darkness, a thick forest comes into view. The tall evergreens seem to reach for the plummeting sleigh. And then it is crashing through the tree-tops, sending snow flying from the branches and the air is filled with the scent of pine resin as needle-clad boughs whip at your face and hands.

Losing control completely, you are no more than a bystander as the lurching sleigh bursts from the forest again, and your ears are deaf to all but the braying screams of the reindeer as the ground rushes up to meet you.

Turn to **195**.

271

Over the keening of the wind and the wailing of the weird sisters, you slowly become aware of a surge of voices, coming up the slope behind you like a flood. Glancing back down the hill, you see a tide of bodies pouring out from Santa's workshop.

Having dealt with their impish rivals, Santa's little helpers mean to take the fight to the Christmas Devil himself. As they charge up the hill, the circling banshees swoop down to meet their challenge, only to find themselves pelted with snowballs.

Turn to **383**.

272

Ask not for whom the bell tolls. It tolls for thee!

You dodge the first dolorous bell, but are not agile enough to avoid the second one as well. It catches you on the backswing, and sends you flying into the wall.

Roll one die and lose this many *Endurance* points; if you roll a 1, deduct 2 *Endurance* points. (Alternatively, pick a card and deduct its face value from your *Endurance* score, unless it is 7 or above, or a picture card, in which case deduct 6 points from your *Endurance* score.)

If you lose 5 *Endurance* points or more, also deduct 1 *Agility* point and 1 *Combat* point.

If you are still alive, turn to **20**.

273

Shrieking at you, her voice the shrill keening of the wind, the elemental spirit that is the Snow Queen attacks, bombarding you with blasts of hail-hard pellets and dagger-sharp shards of ice. (In this battle, the Snow Queen has the initiative.)

SNOW QUEEN	COMBAT 8	ENDURANCE 11

If the Snow Queen wins a Combat Round, roll one die (or pick a card). If the number rolled is odd (or the card is red), you are struck by dagger-shards of ice; lose 2 *Endurance* points. If the number rolled is even (or the card is black), you are bombarded by stinging hail; roll the die again (or pick another card), and if the number rolled is odd (or the card is red), lose 3 *Endurance* points, but if the number rolled is even (or the card is black), lose just 1 *Endurance* point.

If you reduce the Snow Queen's *Endurance* score to 2 or below, she transforms into a flurry of snowflakes that are sent whirling away over the castle wall by a gust of wind – turn to **227**.

274

If you are going to escape the nightmare you now find yourself in, you are going to have to battle the beast lurking below the ice.

If you want to use *The Pen is Mightier* special ability, and still can, turn to **202**. If not, make a note that the Ice Squid has the initiative in the battle to come and turn to **222**.

275

You slide down a chute only a short distance before dropping into an underground chamber, where your fall is broken by a pile of reindeer dung! What an unpleasant place to find yourself, but it least it means you are unhurt.

If you have the code word *Kold* recorded on your Adventure Sheet, turn to **316**. If not, turn to **296**.

276

Before you can reach the door, the pudding explodes. The blast throws you against the wall, and you rebound off it to land in a heap on the floor, as pieces of burning plum pudding rain down around you.

Roll one die and add 2. Deduct this many *Endurance* points. (Alternatively, pick a card and deduct its face value from your *Endurance* score, unless it is 9 or above, or a picture card, in which case deduct 8 points from your *Endurance* score.)

If you have lost a total of 5 *Endurance* points or more, you must also deduct 1 point from your *Agility* score, and if you have lost a total of 7 *Endurance* points or more, also deduct 1 point from your *Combat* score.

If you are still alive, turn to **376**.

277

Each of the three stockings appears to be stuffed with goodies, but you won't actually know precisely what until you stick a hand inside. Which stocking do you want to try first?

The red stocking on the left? Turn to **307**.

The blue stocking in the middle? Turn to **367**.

The green stocking on the right? Turn to **337**.

278

You ride the rails through the factory, ducking overhanging chain links and bracing yourself to resist the swaying motion of the conveyor. Eventually the belt rises in a steep incline, without showing any sign of slowing down, and, as you are fast running out of track, you realise you are going to have to jump for it.

As the conveyor reaches the top of the incline, with nowhere else to go, you fling yourself forwards into space. You land amidst the branches of one of the trees decorating the workshop. But as you start to slip, you grab hold of a string of fairy lights.

As the fairy lights tear free of the tree, you swing down towards the factory floor with an exhilarated cry of "Yippee-ki-yay!" the rest of your shout lost amidst the cacophonous roar of what happens next, as you land on the ground.

Turn to **121**.

279

You have not gone far when a panel opens in the wall and a huge bell swings down from the ceiling across the width of the corridor. A moment later, a second bell descends from the opposite side of the passageway, the two bells tolling as they do so.

If you are going to make it to the other end of the passageway, and the far door, you are going to have to dodge the heavy, swinging bells.

What do you want to do? Will you:

Use the *Naughty or Nice* special ability (if you can)?	Turn to **304**.
Use the Box of Delights (if you have it)?	Turn to **330**.
Attempt to dodge the heavy swinging bells?	Turn to **412**.

280

Following the course described by the bottom of the valley, accompanied by the keening of the wintry wind, you come at last to the shores of the frozen lake.

The most direct route to the castle is across the lake itself.

If you want to set out across the ice, turn to **370**. If you would prefer to skirt the shore of the lake, even though this is a significantly longer route, turn to **200**.

281

Your heart beating a furious tattoo in your chest, like a crazed wind-up tin toy, you prepare to battle the bear. (In this battle, you have the initiative.)

TEDDY BEAR	COMBAT 6	ENDURANCE 6

If you defeat the bear, turn to **242**.

282

You have no choice but to defend yourself as the giant seeks to exact its revenge upon you for all those gingerbread men you have consumed in the past. (In this battle, the Gingerbread Golem has the initiative.)

GINGERBREAD GOLEM	COMBAT 8	ENDURANCE 12

If you manage to defeat the Golem, turn to **327**.

283

Opening the cracked leather tome, you discover that it is a book of imps and demons. Scanning its table of contents, four subjects leap out at you.

Do you want to read about:

Imps?	Turn to **263**.
Krampus, the Christmas Devil?	Turn to **172**.
Snow Sprites?	Turn to **228**.
The Yule Cat?	Turn to **198**.

284

The distraction your intervention has created has weakened Krampus's focus, and therefore the power of the enchantment binding Father Christmas. With the spell waning, the big man has managed to free one of his hands.

Putting his fingers between his lips, Father Christmas gives a shrill whistle, and you manage to tear your eyes from the devil's jaundiced gaze in time to see half a dozen reindeer galloping through the sky towards you. Catching the tattered-rag hags on the prongs of their antlers, they engage Krampus's minions, giving you the chance you need to bring this dark ritual to an abrupt conclusion.

Record the code word *Kringle* on your Adventure Sheet and then turn to **383**.

285

Unfortunately, as far as you are concerned, you are almost at the top of the tower when you fall.

Roll one die, double the number rolled, and lose this many *Endurance* points. (Alternatively, pick a card; if it is 7 or above, or a picture card, it still counts as 6 points. Double the number and lose this many *Endurance* points.)

If you lose 5 *Endurance* points or more, also deduct 1 *Agility* point and 1 *Combat* point. If you lose 7 *Endurance* points or more, also deduct 2 *Agility* points and 1 *Combat* point. And if you lose 9 *Endurance* points or more, also deduct 2 *Agility* points and 2 *Combat* points.

If you somehow manage to survive the fall, turn to **317**.

286

Struggling free of the decorations' stranglehold at last, you stumble across the room and almost fall through the door into the kitchen.

Turn to **5**.

287

As you push the button on the box to the left, you suddenly find yourself hurtling the length of the vast workshop, out of reach of the grasping claws of Satan's little helpers.

Reaching the far end of the factory, you fly through a pair of finely-carved doors into what must be the centre of operations here.

Turn to **485**.

288

You land in a deep snowdrift, sinking deep down into it. Incredibly, it saves you from suffering any injuries at all.

Turn to **344**.

289

The gingerbread you are carrying about your person has a strong, and distinctive, spicy aroma, which reaches the wolves' noses and sets them twitching.

Turn to **339**.

290

The cloaked creature gives a braying cry as you fight it for control of the sleigh. But as you pull on the reins, the team of reindeer swerves sharply left and dives towards the ground.

The wind rushing in your ears, you only become aware of the roar of jet engines when the plane is on top of you. For a moment your gaze meets the shocked stares of the pilot and co-pilot in the cockpit. And then the sleigh swerves sharply out of the airliner's path again, as you pull hard on the reins, struggling to keep control of the panicked reindeer.

Take an Agility test. If you pass the test, turn to **230**, but if you fail the test, turn to **270**.

291

Pushing the knob on the top of the box to the right, you rapidly shrink – your clothes and possessions shrinking with you, as the furniture in the room and the trolls seem to grow, all becoming giants – until you are the size of a cockroach!

You are now small enough to simply walk between the bars of the cage and thus escape captivity.

"Hey, where's supper gone?" one of the trolls suddenly calls out, alerting his brothers to your disappearance.

"There it is!" shouts another, with bulging eyes. "There's the human bean! Get it, lads!"

The trolls all rush to catch you, falling over each other in their haste, as they try to stop you escaping by stamping you underfoot.

You do the only thing you can do – you sprint for shelter under one of the dressers, whilst trying to avoid the trolls' enthusiastic feet.

Take 3 Agility tests! As soon as you fail a test, turn to **331**. However, if you manage to pass all three of the tests, turn to **351**.

292

You choose your moment well, passing between the swinging bells without coming to any harm.

Turn to **20.**

293

The chamber is empty, except for the large box sitting in the middle of the room. Every side is almost five feet in length, and it has been painted in bright colours, with a layer of tough varnish on top.

You can hear the tinkling tune of a wind-up musical box, which appears to be playing 'Pop Goes the Weasel'.

A creeping suspicion comes over you that you are actually standing in front of a huge Jack-in-the-Box, and you hate to think what might emerge when the tune comes to an end.

On the other side of the room there is another door, leading onwards.

What do you want to do? Will you:

Wait and see what happens when the tune finishes playing? Turn to **17**.

Sprint across the room, hoping to reach the far door before the box opens? Turn to **47**.

Climb up on top of the box and sit on the lid, in the hope of stopping it from opening when the tune gets to the end? Turn to **151**.

294

You dodge out of the way of the lashing tentacles, only for them to be withdrawn and the ice rupture elsewhere, nearby, as they re-emerge in a welter of gelid water.

Turn to **182**.

295

With the guards now just so many shards of ice on the floor of the antechamber, you push open the doors and enter a grand throne room. At the end of the chamber, its vaulted roof supported by twisted glacial pillars, seated upon a throne of ice is the ruler of this unreal palace – the Snow Queen!

The monarch of winter is chillingly beautiful, with piercing eyes like sparkling sapphires, while her skin is as white as freshly fallen snow, shot through with ice-blue veins. She is wearing a crown that appears to have been made from sharply-pointed icicles, she is swathed in fur-lined robes and a cloak that looks like it has been fashioned from snowflakes. Indeed, the only human parts of her that can be seen are her angular face and her slender hands.

She fixes you with an icy stare and screams, in a voice as sharp as cut crystal, "How dare you enter the throne room of your queen uninvited!"

The Snow Queen becomes like a blizzard and flies the length of the throne room, as if borne on the wings of Boreas, the North Wind.

You have earned the enmity of the cold-hearted queen and now she is intent on ending you.

If you want to use *The Pen is Mightier* special ability, and you still can, turn to **9**. If not, turn to **273**.

296

It is much warmer here than it was outside.

(Restore up to 2 *Endurance* points, 1 *Agility* point, and 1 *Combat* point.)

Now turn to **316**.

297

You hold the lantern up before you, abruptly stopping the snowmen in their tracks. But it's not long before they start to creep forward again.

If you are going to escape this place, you are going to have to fight the snowmen, but as long as you are holding the lantern out before you, their resolve will be weakened and they will be easier to defeat.

(Make a note that when you finally face your abominable foes to combat, you may reduce their *Combat* scores by 1 point each.)

Now turn to **489**.

298

Jack Frost's icy touch numbs your flesh. For every successful strike he makes against you, as well as deducting 2 *Endurance* points, you must also deduct 1 *Combat* point.

Now return to **268** and continue your battle with the ice elemental.

299

Before you can get back to the safety of the thicker ice beside the bridge, the fractured, frozen surface gives way under you, plunging you into the sub-zero waters of the river.

Take an Endurance test. If you pass the test, turn to **24**. If you fail the test, turn to **44**.

300

Reaching the far side of the kitchen, you push open the double doors and leave the sickly-sweet cloying atmosphere behind.

On the other side is a flight of stone steps. Climbing these you open another door and are assailed by the clattering, chugging and crashing of a factory production line running at full tilt.

Turn to **418**.

301

The conveyor suddenly starts to speed up, and you are forced to focus all your attention on simply not being thrown off!

Take an Agility test, but deduct 1 from the dice roll. If you end up passing the test, turn to **278**, but if you fail the test, turn to **259**.

302

Although nothing on the kitchen counters or worktops appears to have been disturbed, there are scuff marks on the floor, smears of mud, and what looks like soot as well. Amongst all this mess you find two distinct footprints; one made by a human foot and the other a large hoof-print, like that of some cloven-footed creature.

The sight unsettles you deeply, and your mind goes back to the thud you heard upon waking, when the clock in the hall chimed thirteen. You start to wonder if the interloper raided the kitchen cupboards, and open them to have a look.

There's no sign that anyone rummaged through the cupboards, and the turkey is still in the refrigerator, along with the pigs in blankets, ready to go in the oven in the morning, but the sight of all those packets of savoury snacks makes your mouth water.

If you want to help yourself to some of the snacks and make a midnight feast of it, turn to **322**. Otherwise, will you open the back door, in the hope of catching whoever was just in here (turn to **342**), or run back upstairs to bed and hide under the covers (turn to **98**)?

303

Hauling yourself into the ice cave, sheltered from the wind at last, you rest for a moment. (Now would be a good time to eat a Meal or have a drink, if you can.)

As you take in your surroundings, you see strange carvings etched into the undulating walls of blue ice that form a tunnel, which in turn penetrates deeper into the glacier.

Intrigued, and wondering what the symbols can mean, you follow the tunnel through the ice. An eerie blue glow seems to come from inside the ice itself, enabling you to see where you are going, no matter how far you are from the moonlit entrance to the cave.

The tunnel eventually enters a chamber at the heart of the glacier. And there, suspended in a shaft of silvery moonlight that enters through a narrow hole in the ceiling, is a most magnificent sword.

It appears to be made entirely from ice, and has snowflake-like patterns carved into the blue-white material of its blade. You have never seen anything like it!

Snow has drifted into the icy alcoves of the chamber, having entered through the shaft in the roof as well, you imagine, while icicles hang down from the ceiling like frozen stalactites.

If you want to try to reach into the beam of moonlight and take the sword, turn to **336**. If you would prefer to leave the clearly magical frozen blade where it is, turn to **363**.

304

You move towards the clanging chimes as if put into a hypnotic state by the dolorous tolling of the Christmas bells. But in this trance-like state, your perception of time speeds up and the swinging of the bells seems to slow, in defiance of gravity, and so you can see precisely when it is safe to step through the gap between them.

In this way, you pass safely between the swinging bells.

Cross off one use of the *Naughty or Nice* special ability and turn to **20**.

305

What do you have that you think the cat might want? Will you offer it:

Food (if you have some)?	Turn to **325**.
A wooden box (if you have one)?	Turn to **345**.
An item of clothing?	Turn to **365**.
A weapon (if you have one)?	Turn to **77**.

If you cannot offer the ferocious feline any of these items, or do not want to give them up, turn to **157**.

306

You carefully fill a glass with the warmed wine, and drink it down. You savour the aromatic concoction as it warms you from the inside. You suspect you will enjoy the benefits of its effects for some time to come.

Gain 2 *Endurance* points and, if you have the code word *Kold* written on your Adventure Sheet, cross it off now.

What would you like to do now?

Take a look at the book?	Turn to **283**.
Leave the cottage without further ado?	Turn to **355**.

307

You reach into the stocking…

There is a sudden, sharp *SNAP!* and a spasm of pain shoots up your arm, almost making you cry out in shock. Pulling your hand out again, you see that your throbbing fingers have been caught in a mousetrap that someone had hidden inside the stocking!

You prise the trap open, freeing your fingers, but the damage has already been done. Your digits are swollen, bruised and bleeding. (Lose 1 *Combat* point and 2 *Endurance* points.)

Deciding not to go near any of the other stockings, you move on to look at the tree instead.

Turn to **395**.

308

If you have any uses of your *Naughty or Nice* special ability left, turn to **300**. If not, turn to **332**.

309

Roll one die (or pick a card). If the number rolled is odd (or the card is red), turn to **67**. If the number rolled is even (or the card is black), turn to **114**.

310

There's no time to delay. You are sure the succubus is on her way to alert your quarry to your progress.

"Your destination lies to the north, beyond the mountains," the blacksmith tells you, "but betwixt here and there lies a forest and a frozen lake. It will be up to you to decide which path to follow, but both will ultimately bring you to the river of ice that marks the pass through the mountains. Good luck!"

Thanking the blacksmith for his help, you set off into the night, heading north as directed.

Turn to **484**.

311

The polished wooden box the Punch and Judy Man gave you might be your only hope. Taking it from your dressing-gown pocket, you regard the brass button on the lid.

If you can remember what to do to go small, and you still want to use the box, do it now. If you can't remember, or you don't want to use it after all, turn back to **254** and try something else.

312

As you approach the antechamber, the ice-formed guards start to move, with an unnatural life of their own, bringing their glittering polearms to bear. If you want to enter the chamber they are guarding, you are going to have to fight your way through.

If you want to change your mind and leave the keep again, hoping that the guards don't follow you, turn to **381**. If you want to bring *The Pen is Mightier* special ability to bear, and you still can, turn to **262**. If you are prepared to fight the guardians to achieve your goal, turn to **224**.

313

You cannot resist the dread power of the Snow Queen and, in only a matter of moments, your flesh, along with the blood in your veins, has frozen solid. You will remain in the winter witch's sculpture garden until Hell freezes over.

Your adventure is over.

The End

314

No matter how hard you struggle, you cannot free yourself from the cephalopod's constricting tentacles. You can only look on in abject terror as the abyssal horror surfaces, breaking through the ice, and pulls you within reach of its snapping beak.

With bone-crunching power, the lake monster bites down hard!

Roll one die and add 2. Deduct this many *Endurance* points. (Alternatively, pick a card and deduct its face value from your *Endurance* score, unless it is 9 or above, or a picture card, in which case deduct 8 points from your *Endurance* score.)

If you have lost a total of 5 *Endurance* points or more, you must also deduct 1 point from your *Agility* score, and if you have lost a total of 7 *Endurance* points or more, also deduct 1 point from your *Combat* score.

If you are still alive, as the squid loosens its hold, you manage to struggle free of its coils at last.

Turn to **274**.

315

Roll one die (or pick a card). If the number rolled is odd (or the card is red), turn to **339**. If the number rolled is even (or the card is black), turn to **378**.

316

Climbing down from the top of the mound of manure, you make your way along an underground passageway which ends at a small chamber. The only interesting features of the room are the two doors leading from it.

Both bear painted wooden plaques, but the one on the left-hand door reads 'TOYS' while the sign on the door on the right reads 'GAMES'.

You doubt you could climb the slippery chute back up to the trapdoor, so the only way onwards is through one of the doors in front of you. But which door will you choose? The one marked 'TOYS' (turn to **432**), or the one marked 'GAMES' (turn to **142**)?

317

You pick yourself up again, feeling every bump and bruise you have sustained; you even suspect you might have cracked a rib or two.

If you want to try to scale the tower again, turn to **397**. If you would rather go somewhere else, turn to **381**.

318

What you at first took to be a blanket of snow on the ground are in fact the snow-clad branches of a pine forest.

You hit a bough, which breaks under the impact, sending snow showering down around you as you continue to tumble through the pine-scented, needle-bristling trees.

The snowy branches help to slow your fall, but they also break your body in return, battering and bruising your limbs.

Roll one die and add 3. Deduct this many *Endurance* points. (Alternatively, pick a card and deduct its face value from your *Endurance* score, unless it is a 10 or a picture card, in which case deduct 9 points from your *Endurance* score; if it is less than 4 you must deduct 4 *Endurance* points.)

If you have lost 5-7 *Endurance* points, you must also deduct 1 point from both your *Agility* score and your *Combat* score.

If you have lost 8-9 *Endurance* points, you must also deduct 2 points from both your *Agility* score and your *Combat* score.

If you are still alive, turn to **344**.

319

Under the Gremlin's relentless assault, you stumble backwards off the edge of the conveyor belt and hit the floor hard, landing on your back. (Lose 3 *Endurance* points.)

If you are still alive, turn to **463**.

320

The cloaked creature gives a braying cry as you fight it for control of the sleigh. But as you pull on the reins, the team of reindeer swerves sharply left and dives towards the ground.

The wind rushing in your ears, you only become aware of the roar of jet engines when the plane is on top of you. For a moment your gaze meets the shocked stares of the pilot and co-pilot in the cockpit, and then the sleigh swerves sharply out of the airliner's path again, rolling as the reindeer describe a spiralling path through the blizzard.

The reins slip from your hands, you slide from your seat on the driver's bench, and suddenly you are tumbling through the snow-swept sky, dropping like a stone towards the ground.

Turn to **235**.

321

(Cross off one use of the *Naughty or Nice* special ability.)

To your horror, other toys in the room start to come to life, climbing out of boxes or dropping down from the shelves, all of them moving towards you.

"Mama!" cries a grinning clown doll as it strides stiff-legged towards you, and a wind-up ballerina dances across the room, while the wooden jaws of a crocodile puppet go *clack-clack-clack* at it approaches.

You have no choice but to fight your way past the animated toys. (In this battle, the toys have the initiative, and you must fight them two at a time, starting with the first two.)

	COMBAT	ENDURANCE
TEDDY BEAR	6	6
CLOCKWORK BALLERINA	5	5
CLOWN DOLL	6	5
CROCODILE PUPPET	5	6

If you manage to defeat all of the toys, or after 15 Combat Rounds, whichever is sooner, turn to **242**.

322

You load the capacious pockets of your dressing gown with enough snacks for a fabulous feast. (Add 4 Meals to your Adventure Sheet.)

What do you want to do now? Will you open the back door, in the hope of catching whoever was just in here (turn to **342**), or run back upstairs to bed and hide under the covers (turn to **98**)?

323

The door of the cottage suddenly bursts open and a figure rushes through it, accompanied by a flurry of snowflakes. It is an old crone, bent almost double by a dowager's stoop.

Ignoring you, she takes the broomstick she is carrying and hits the ice hobgoblin with it, crying out, "Begone, Jack Frost!" as she does so.

The home-invader gives a cry and breaks into a whirlwind of ice crystals that blows out through the open window, into the freezing night.

(Record the code word *Krafty* on your Adventure Sheet.)

The old witch bustles over to the window, pulling it shut and fixing the latch. She then turns on you, demanding, "Who are you? Were you sent by *him?*"

"Him?" you repeat, flustered.

"Yes, him! You do know who *he* is, don't you?"

"Um… Yes, of course I do," you reply uncertainly.

"Who is he then?" the crone demands, raising her broomstick, ready to hit you next.

Not wishing to risk antagonising the witch any further, how will you answer?

"Krampus." Turn to **375**.

"Father Christmas." Turn to **406**.

324

Try as you might, you cannot break free of the devil's mesmerising stare.

"I see it, I swear, that your soul is unclean,
So come, join us now, and our coven's thirteen!"

You cannot break the sinister hold the Christmas Devil has over you. Rather than resist the demon and rescue Father Christmas, you actually help Krampus break Santa's power, as the dark rite reaches its climax, and the festive season will never be the same again.

You have fallen at the final hurdle. Your adventure is over.

The End

325

You throw the food in front of the cat, which promptly proceeds to gobble it up, every last crumb. (Cross off 1 Meal.) While the feline is distracted, what do you want to do?

Run away? Turn to **157**.

Offer it something else? Turn to **365**.

Attack the animal? Turn to **77**.

326

You unfold the piece of parchment, which crackles as you do so, and read the words written upon it in glittering black ink, in an ornate gothic hand.

My dear La Befana,

I hope this missive finds you well in the lead up to what is our busiest time of year.

I am writing to you because I have concerns about our mutual acquaintance, Mr Krampus. From what little communication I have had with the old goat recently, he seems very disgruntled with his appointed role.

This unhappiness appears to stem from the fact that many people do not mark his special night, Krampusnacht, on 5th December anymore, and many children do not even know his name.

I think he is planning something and would ask that you keep an eye out for any sign of impish activity whilst out on your travels.

Thank you and I wish you all the blessings of the season.

Your friend

F. C.

You stare at the piece of parchment, barely able to believe your eyes, let along what you are reading.

What do you want to do now? Will you:

Sample some of the spiced, mulled wine (if you haven't already done so)?	Turn to **306**.
Take a look at the book?	Turn to **283**.
Leave the cottage before its owner returns?	Turn to **355**.

327

The Gingerbread Golem is down, and doesn't get up again. As the goblin kitchen staff look on in disbelief, you set off once more.

Turn to **300**.

328

If you want to use *The Pen is Mightier* special ability now, cross off one use and turn to **403** at once.

If you do not, and you have the code word *Kritical* written on your Adventure Sheet, turn to **386**; otherwise, turn to **459**.

329

Not waiting for the thin ice to give way while you are still standing on it, you race back the way you came, back to the safety of the frost fair's environs.

Turn to **64**.

330

Perhaps the box could help you out of your current dire predicament.

If you know what you need to do to go swift, do it now. If you don't know, or you don't want to go swift, you will have to try something else.

Will you use the *Naughty or Nice* special ability, if you can (turn to **304**), or will you attempt to dodge the swinging bells (turn to **412**)?

331

There are simply too many stamping feet to avoid and it is only a matter of time before one of them comes down on top of you, crushing you against the hard stone floor of the cave.

Roll one die and add 3. Deduct this many *Endurance* points. (Alternatively, pick a card and deduct its face value from your *Endurance* score, unless it is a 10 or a picture card, in which case deduct 9 points from your *Endurance* score; if it is less than 4 you must deduct 4 *Endurance* points.)

If you have lost 5-7 *Endurance* points, you must also deduct 1 point from both your *Agility* score and your *Combat* score.

If you have lost 8-9 *Endurance* points, you must also deduct 2 points from both your *Agility* score and your *Combat* score.

If you are still alive, turn to **351**.

332

It's no good, you can't resist the delectable delights arrayed on the tables, and swipe a toffee apple from a cooling rack.

(Record the Toffee Apple on your Adventure Sheet. It is equivalent to 1 Meal.)

But as you continue to crawl across the kitchen, using the tables for cover, you become aware of a high-pitched chuntering noise coming from behind you.

Still on your hands and knees, you glance behind you. Several table-lengths away, half a dozen gingerbread men are scouring the tiled floor. Their iced expressions are twisted into unwelcoming grimaces. It would seem that the kitchen has its own half-baked guardians.

Scrambling from under the table, you duck into an alcove, hoping to escape the attention of the gingerbread men. But your decision is more a case of out of the frying pan and into the fire, than getting away by the skin of your teeth. Racks and racks of the cinnamon-spiced cookie creations drop down from the shelves in the alcove to attack. One of them even lands on your shoulder and bites you before you can shake it off. (Lose 2 *Endurance* points.)

How do you want to deal with this new threat? Do you want to try offering the gingerbread men something, in the hope of appeasing them (turn to **217**), or will you prepare to defend yourself once again (turn to **419**)?

333

Against the odds, or so it would seem, you resist the freezing power of the Snow Queen's magic, although it drains you of a portion of your strength nonetheless.

(Lose 2 *Endurance* points and 1 *Combat* point.)

If you are still alive, your teeth chattering in your skull, you prepare to resist the ice witch.

If you want to use *The Pen is Mightier* special ability now, and you still can, turn to **9**. If not, turn to **273**.

334

Unable to evade the writhing tentacles, you are caught in their gelid embrace, and gasp for air as they squeeze the breath from your body.

You only have one option, and that is to try to fight your way free.

Take an Endurance test and a *Combat* test. If you fail either test, turn to **314**. However, if you pass both tests, turn to **274**.

335

A host of potential foes stands between you and the rescue of Father Christmas. You are vastly outnumbered – at least ten to one, if not more – and it is surely only a matter of time before one of Krampus's minions launches an attack against you.

If you have the code word *Kourageous* recorded on your Adventure Sheet, turn to **271**. If not, turn to **481**.

336

Tentatively, you reach into the beam and, feeling no ill-effects, take hold of the pommel of the ice sword. There is a moment's resistance, and then you pull the blade free.

You marvel at the intricate patterns adorning the blade, wondering who made it, and how it ended up hidden within a cave inside the glacier.

A sound like someone shuffling through the snow takes your attention from the blade and back to your immediate surroundings.

As you watch, the drifts of snow form themselves into two roughly humanoid shapes. Despite having no obvious legs, these crude snowmen shuffle towards you. As they do so, spears of ice emerge from the ends of snow-formed arms and appear within the gaping maws yawning in their blunt heads, and you realise that by taking the Ice Sword you have provoked the ire of the elemental spirits that guard this place.

What do you want to do? Will you:

Try to return the Ice Sword to the shaft of moonlight?	Turn to **348**.
Use a lantern to keep the snowmen back (if you have one?)	Turn to **297**.
Use the Box of Delights (if you have it)?	Turn to **468**.
Use the *Naughty or Nice* special ability (if you still can)?	Turn to **368**.
Use *The Pen is Mightier* special ability (if you still can)?	Turn to **428**.
Fight the snowmen?	Turn to **489**.

337

The stocking has been filled with nuts and fruit. A little chocolate or some sweets might have been nice, but there is enough food to make up one Meal. (Add this Meal to your Adventure Sheet.)

Do you want to dip a hand into one of the other stockings (turn to **307**), or would you rather take a look at the Christmas tree now (turn to **395**)?

338

The Gremlin looks at you with a gleeful smile on its face, as it reaches for you with hands that end in cruel-looking claws. (In this battle, the Gremlin has the initiative.)

GREMLIN	COMBAT 7	ENDURANCE 6

As you are having to fight the Gremlin whilst trying to keep your balance on a fast-moving conveyor belt, for the duration of this battle only, when calculating your *Combat Rating* you must deduct 1 point.

If the Gremlin scores two consecutive strikes against you, turn to **319** at once.

If you manage to defeat the Gremlin within 6 Combat Rounds, turn to **301**. If not, after 6 Combat Rounds turn to **357**.

339

A keening howl cuts through the blizzard, alerting you to the fact that the wolves have sniffed you out. Leaving the reindeer's carcass, they lope towards you over the snow.

Do you want to run for it (turn to **449**), or will you stand your ground ready to fight (turn to **19**)?

340

Taking your life in your hands, and with your heart in your mouth, you scramble over the piles of bulging sacks. The driver remains ignorant to the fact that you are loose in the back of the sleigh, until it is too late.

Grabbing the reins, you try to wrestle them out of the creature's hands.

Take a Combat test, and if you pass the test, turn to **290**, but if you fail the test, turn to **320**.

341

The instant the three numbers align, accompanied by a rumbling, grating noise, part of the stone-flagged floor irises open, revealing a pit beneath. And lying in the pit is a magnificent spear, fashioned from the wood of the mistletoe. You notice that twelve bands have been carved around the shaft at irregularly spaced intervals.

(Record the Mistletoe Spear on your Adventure Sheet, along with the fact that it is circled by twelve bands.)

"Guard it well," says Holly.

"And it will guard you well," says Ivy.

Taking your prize with you, with no other way back down the tower, you climb out of the window and descend to the courtyard below.

Turn to **381**.

342

There's soot on the handle of the back door too, where someone has opened it from the inside.

Pulling open the door yourself, you peer out into the ice-cold night, half-closing your eyes against the biting wind. Snow lies thick on the ground, blanketing everything in fuzzy white anonymity. The wind is howling about the eaves of the house and sending flurries of flakes rushing into your face.

And then you hear the clanking of chains and glance upwards. Following the sound to its source, you catch a glimpse of something large and shadowy, as it climbs up onto the roof and disappears.

Your heart racing and your frantic breath clouding in the air in front of you, you feel your blood quicken as your system is flooded with adrenalin, your body preparing itself to either fight or flee. But which is it to be?

If you want to climb up the drainpipe and follow whatever it was that you just saw scramble onto the roof, turn to **382**. If you would prefer to slam the door and hurry back to bed, turn to **98**.

343

You are standing in a tiny room with pine-clad walls. Checking the door by which you entered, you discover that it is locked – and there is no keyhole!

In front of you, however, are two more doors, identical in every way except that on one has been painted the word 'Six' and on the other is the word 'Seven'. Above the doors, a colourful sign reads:

How many Swans-a-Swimming?

Clearly only one of the answers presented on the doors can be correct and you imagine it would be wise to choose the door bearing the right one. So which door is it to be?

'Six'? Turn to **436**.

'Seven'? Turn to **372**.

344

Once you have taken a moment to compose yourself after your dramatic fall, you take a look around you.

You are in the depths of a forest. Snow covers the ground and the trees, and continues to fall from the sky, muffling all sound apart from the crunch of the stuff under your feet. What you wouldn't do for a pair of snow boots right now!

If you have the code word *Kosy* recorded on your Adventure Sheet, turn to **364**. If not, turn to **384**.

345

You take out the Box of Delights and wave it at the cat. The creature immediately crouches down, before making a sudden leap and knocking the box from your hands. The trinket flies through the air and hits a stone projecting from the snow, breaking into pieces on contact.

(Strike the Box of Delights from your Equipment list.)

Seemingly angry that its toy has broken so easily, the cat turns on you.

Turn to **137**.

346

You carefully fill a glass with the warmed wine, and drink it down. You savour the aromatic concoction as it warms you from the inside. You suspect you will enjoy the benefits of its effects for some time to come.

Gain 2 *Endurance* points and, if you have the code word *Kold* written on your Adventure Sheet, cross it off now.

What would you like to do now?

Read the letter?	Turn to **326**.
Take a look at the book?	Turn to **283**.
Leave the cottage without further ado?	Turn to **213**.

347

And then suddenly Father Christmas is there, standing over the defeated devil, looking like some mighty Teutonic god of old. He takes hold of one of Krampus's chains and binds the demon with it, as he starts to chant something in what you think might be Latin.

As he does so, the top of the hill splits open, and you are hit by a gust of scalding air that rises from its hellish depths. You watch in awe, as the saint picks up the demon, raising him above his head before casting his vanquished foe into the pit with a shout of, "Begone, Satan!"

Turn to **500.**

348

As the snowmen continue to shuffle towards you, you hold the Ice Sword in the beam of moonlight, but it will not remain in place. Either you have broken the spell that kept it suspended there, or the sword *wants* you to have it.

And so, taking a firm grip on the pommel, you prepare to chop the snowmen into flakes with the ice-sharp blade. But then you see another snowy guardian taking form within the cave.

Do you want to use *The Pen is Mightier* special ability, if you can (turn to **428**), or will you engage all three of the snowmen in battle (turn to **388**)?

349

Roll one die (or pick a card). If the number rolled is odd (or the card is red), turn to **299**. If the number rolled is even (or the card is black), turn to **329**.

350

Pushing the button to the left, you rocket along the passageway and, before any more obstacles can appear in your way, you find yourself standing in front of the door at the far end.

Turn to **492**.

351

Throwing yourself under the dresser, you spy a crack in the cave wall, and feel a cold breeze blowing through it. It must lead outside!

Not wanting to remain in the troll's cave a moment longer, you stagger towards the fissure. But before you can reach it, something scampers into your path, blocking your way out.

It is a rat, only to you it now appears to be as big as an elephant! The rodent gives a shrill squeak, baring long, yellow, chisel-like teeth, and goes for you.

If you want to use *The Pen is Mightier* special ability, and still can, turn to **135**. If not, turn to **174**.

352

A shouted curse in Italian has you looking to the sky again. Zooming through the cold, crisp air on her broomstick comes the kindly witch, and Father Christmas's ancient ally, La Befana.

You are delighted to see the old woman, but Krampus's allies aren't. The circling banshees cry out in alarm and anger as La Befana flies into their midst, unleashing powerful magic with dramatic flourishes of her wand, and keeping them busy.

Turn to **383**.

353

Suddenly shrieking like a banshee, white-feathered wings flapping furiously, the malevolent puppet launches itself at you, and you are forced to defend yourself as best you can. (In this battle your attacker has the initiative.)

PERCHTA	COMBAT 7	ENDURANCE 6

If you have not defeated the Perchta after five Combat Rounds, turn to **90**. However, if you manage to dispatch the giggling fairy in fewer than five Combat Rounds, turn to **373**.

354

Pushing the button to the right, you rapidly shrink in stature, until you are no taller than a mouse. In your new diminutive form, you scamper across the antechamber and under the doors, unseen by the chamber's frozen guardians.

You are standing at the far end of a palatial throne room. Like the rest of the keep, everything here is made of ice, from the fluted columns to the vaulted roof they support.

Seated upon a throne, carved from a single block of ice, is the ruler of this frozen palace – the Snow Queen! The monarch of winter is chillingly beautiful, with piercing eyes like sparkling sapphires, while her skin is as white as freshly fallen snow, shot through with ice-blue veins. She is wearing a crown that appears to have been made from sharply-pointed icicles, she is swathed in fur-lined robes and a cloak that looks like it has been fashioned from snowflakes. Indeed, the only human parts of her that can be seen are her angular face and her slender hands.

If you have the code word *Krafty* recorded on your Adventure Sheet, turn to **54**. If not, turn to **154**.

355

The door of the cottage suddenly bursts open and a figure rushes through it, accompanied by a flurry of snowflakes. It is an old crone, bent almost double by a dowager's stoop, and wrapped up against the cold under a dozen layers of shawls and coats.

Raising the broomstick she is holding in her hands, she shrieks, "Who are you and what are you doing in my home? Were you sent by *him?*"

"Him?" you repeat, flustered.

"Yes, him! You do know who *he* is, don't you?"

"Um… Yes, of course I do," you reply uncertainly.

"Who is he then?" the crone demands, raising her broomstick, ready to hit you next.

Not wishing to risk antagonising the witch any further, how will you answer?

"Krampus."	Turn to **375**.
"Father Christmas."	Turn to **406**.

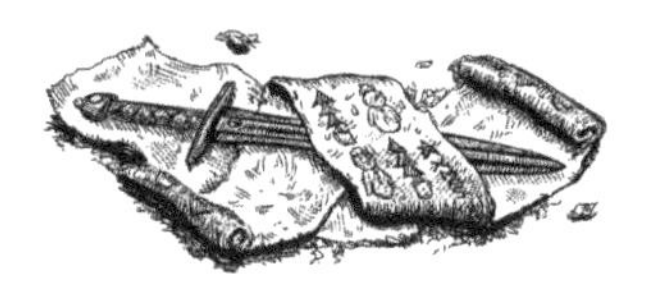

356

It is still bitterly cold outside, and despite pulling the collar of your dressing-gown up to keep out the icy wind, soon your teeth are chattering and your arms and legs are shivering.

(Deduct 2 *Endurance* points, 1 *Agility* point, and 1 *Combat* point.)

Now turn to **483**.

357

Rather unexpectedly, the conveyor starts to speed up. Taken by surprise, the Gremlin loses its balance and topples off the belt backwards. Its strangled cry is abruptly cut off as it falls into the grinding guts of the machinery.

You have to fight to retain your balance too as the conveyor runs faster and faster.

Take an Agility test, and if you pass the test, turn to **278**. However, if you fail the test, turn to **259**.

358

Snarling, the blood of the reindeer having turned their muzzles red, the wolves attack!

If you want to use *The Pen is Mightier* special ability, and you still can, turn to **52**. If not, make a note that the wolves have the initiative and then turn to **203**.

359

It is then that you spot the pan of milk that has been left to warm on the hot plate of a stove. Making a lunge for it, and seizing the wooden handle with both hands, you pull it off the heat and hurl its contents over the advancing gingerbread men.

When you mix hot milk and cookies, the outcome is inevitable. Squealing pitifully, the biscuit people rapidly start to dissolve, and soon they are nothing more than a gloopy, crumbly mess on the floor.

The goblin cooks are aware of your presence now too, but you are determined to escape the kitchens before they can catch you.

Cross off one use of your *The Pen is Mightier* special ability and turn to **300**.

360

Scrambling over the piles of bulging sacks, you launch a surprise attack on the driver.

Make a note that you have the initiative in the forthcoming battle and turn to **131**.

361

You suddenly find yourself beset by a whirling blizzard. The freezing wind tugs at your clothes and hair, and you are forced to half-close your eyes against the stinging cold.

But then you see a face within the snowstorm, a chillingly beautiful face, and you realise that the howling of the gale is actually a shrieking scream.

By trespassing here, you have earned the enmity of the mistress of this place, the ruler of the ice-clad castle, the frozen-hearted Snow Queen herself!

As you come to understand who your attacker is, you also realise that she intends to freeze you to death where you stand, and turn you into another of her tortured ice sculptures!

Take an Endurance test and a Combat test, as you fight the freezing effects of her sub-zero sorcery.

If you pass both tests, turn to **333**, but if you fail *either* test, turn to **313** at once.

362

Making your way along the lantern-lit corridor, you eventually come to a set of double doors which swing open at your touch, and you find yourself at the entrance to a cavernous kitchen.

Everywhere you look, strange, overweight goblin-like creatures, wearing food-stained aprons and tall chef's hats, are preparing platters of the most marvellous confections. You can see trays of marzipan fruits, candy canes, meringues, candied fruits and toffee apples, as well as the most magnificent jellies, bowls of boiled sweets, mountains of mince pies, doughnuts, cakes and cream horns.

The sight of the sublime sweetmeats and the delectable syrupy scent that fills the air have your mouth watering in moments.

A great oven bathes the kitchen in its infernal glow, whilst making it almost unbearably hot for someone wearing a dressing-gown.

On the far side of the kitchen stands a set of double doors, which you hope will lead you up to Father Christmas's workshop.

The kitchen is so chaotically busy that you are confident you could sneak across it – ducking under tables and behind pillars as required – and escape without being spotted by the curious confectioners.

And so you set off, dropping to your hands and knees to crawl under a table when a goblin chef walks past carrying a tray of iced buns. It would be easy to snaffle a prize from one of the trays of tempting treats as you make your way through the kitchen.

Do you want to give in to temptation and help yourself to a cooling toffee apple (turn to **332**), or will you attempt to make your way across the kitchen without giving in to temptation (turn to **308**)?

363

On the other side of the ice cave, the tunnel continues on its undulating way through the glacier, and you follow it until you eventually emerge on the far side, at the northern edge of the mountain pass.

You make your way through the mountains until the ground underfoot starts to slope downwards and you find yourself looking out across a vast ice-sheet. And there, not half a league away, you see the flickering of candle-light coming from the windows of a vast structure of stone and wood. It must be Santa's workshop!

Turn to **100**.

364

You might not have any snow boots, but you do have a woolly hat, knitted scarf, and gloves, from the parcel you unwrapped under the tree, and so you quickly pull them on.

Turn to **414**.

365

What do you want to give the cat? One of your old slippers (turn to **177**), or your new scarf (turn to **385**)?

366

Turning a handle that looks like an iced doughnut, you open the door and enter the cottage.

Despite what its exterior might have led you to believe, inside it appears to be a normal cottage, with wooden floorboards, walls made of interlocking pine planks, and a stone-built chimney breast.

Warming on a black iron stove is a saucepan containing a dark red liquid, that fills the air with the heady smell of wine, cloves, nutmeg and orange zest.

Facing the fire is a rocking chair, and next to that stands a small table. Lying on top of it is a large book and an open, hand-written letter.

It is clear that whoever lives here is not home at present, but it also looks like they've only popped out for a moment and could return at any time.

Do you want to:

Sample some of the mulled wine warming on the stove?	Turn to **346**.
Read the letter?	Turn to **326**.
Take a look at the book?	Turn to **283**.
Leave the cottage before its owner returns?	Turn to **213**.

367

Roll one die (or pick a card). If the number rolled is odd (or the card is red), turn to **307**. If the number rolled is even (or the card is black), turn to **337**.

368

(Cross off one use of the *Naughty or Nice* special ability.)

As the snowmen close on your position, bathed in the eerie silvery moonlight, you see another snowy simulacrum take form within the cave.

Do you want to use *The Pen is Mightier* special ability, if you can (turn to **428**), or will you engage all three of the snowmen in battle (turn to **388**)?

369

Krampus leans closer, his long pock-marked tongue writhing from his fanged mouth as if with a life of its own, and you almost retch as the devil's breath comes at you in rancid gusts.

You cannot help but meet his horribly bulging yellow eyes and stare into the pinpricks of darkness that are the pupils within.

"I'll ask you just once – I'll not ask you twice –
Have you, my child, been naughty or nice?"

Take a Combat test. If you pass the test, turn to **284**. If you fail the test, turn to **324**.

370

Taking your first tentative steps out onto the ice, you soon relax as it becomes clear that it is thick enough to support your weight.

You are halfway across the lake, about as far away from solid ground as you can be, when you become aware of something moving beneath you. Looking down through the thick ice, by the light of the full moon shining overhead, you almost jump out of your skin when you see a huge saucer-shaped eye staring back at you.

Startled by its appearance, do you want to sprint for the far shore (turn to **393**), or do you want to try to overcome your flight response, and remain perfectly motionless, exactly where you are (turn to **443**)?

371

Taking out the set of Lockpicks you recovered from the giant cracker, while the trolls are busying themselves laying the long wooden table for supper, you set to work.

Waggling and jiggling the tools in the lock, your efforts are soon rewarded with a sharp click and the door of the cage swings open.

You're not going to get a better opportunity than this, so you burst out of the cage and run for the door.

Turn to **199**.

372

As soon as you are through the door, it slams shut behind you. You are in another small room with two more near-identical doors in front of you, but this time, the question painted on the facing wall reads:

What were the names of the three Kings?

Three names are painted on each of the doors, but which door will you choose?

'Melchior, Caspar, Balthazar'? Turn to **392**.

'Melchior, Caspar, Belshazzar'? Turn to **456**.

373

Seizing hold of the sinister doll, you hurl it across the room, where it lands amidst the embers of the dying fire, throwing up a flurry of sparks.

The flames rise once more, fed by the articulated wooden body and flammable dress, and the thing's insane giggling only reaches new heights of hysteria as the possessed puppet burns.

Shaken by the experience, you stumble from the sitting room through the door into the kitchen.

Record the code word *Kreepy* on your Adventure Sheet and then turn to **5**.

374

You are convinced that whatever lies beyond those doors of ice must be important, and the box might be the way for you to gain access.

If you can remember what to do to go small, do it now. If you can't remember, or you would prefer to quit the keep and search elsewhere, turn to **381**. If you don't remember but are nonetheless determined to pass beyond the double doors, turn to **312**.

375

"I knew it!" spits the witch and, muttering something under her breath, hits you with the broomstick.

You immediately shrink inside your pyjamas and fall to the ground, landing on four feet. Pushing your way out from under the mound of your clothes, you peer up at the witch – who looks like a giantess to you now – through large, moist, amphibian eyes and give an anxious croak.

The old crone has turned you into a frog! Your adventure is over.

The End

376

Picking yourself up off the floor, you survey the devastation all around you. Those pieces of pudding not burned black by the explosion look quite delicious.

If you want, you may scavenge enough pieces of Christmas pudding to make 2 Meals.

Once you are done, knowing that your adventure is not over yet, you leave the room through the far door, wondering what other secrets are hiding within Santa's workshop.

Turn to **492**.

377

Fearing the worst, and no longer caring that the goblin cooks might see you, you stumble from your hiding place, staring up at the gigantic gingerbread man in horror!

Following you from your hiding place, the agglomeration of gingerbread, which is only just able to stand upright without scraping its head on the ceiling, storms after you, upending tables and sending trays of food flying.

The goblin cooks scatter before the Gingerbread Golem's advance. But the hulking colossus isn't concerned about them – its only concern is that you do not escape it.

How on earth are you going to defend yourself against a giant, malevolent, biscuit person?

Will you:

Use the Box of Delights (if you have it)?	Turn to **63**.
Throw something at the Gingerbread Golem?	Turn to **85**.
Sprint for the double doors on the other side of the kitchen?	Turn to **208**.
Tempt fate by using your *Naughty or Nice* special ability (if you still can)?	Turn to **194**.
Prepare to fight the colossal confection?	Turn to **264**.

378

The wolves are so engrossed in tearing the reindeer's carcass apart, their noses buried in its viscera, they do not notice you as you creep past, to vanish again moments later, into the night.

Turn to **83**.

As you are wondering how you are going to escape the desperate situation you now find yourself in, you hear the sound of breaking glass as something smashes through one of the mullioned windows of the workshop. Looking up, you see a reindeer fly into the factory, galloping through the air on hooves that send a fine silvery powder cascading into the space with every airborne beat.

It's Comet! Before you have really grasped what is happening, the reindeer swoops down and, grabbing its neck, you throw yourself onto its back. Comet doesn't pause for a second, but takes to the air again, as the first of the bombs detonates, initiating a chain reaction.

As devastating fireballs bloom within the workshop, tearing apart the clanking conveyors – the resulting falling burning debris setting fire to the piles of presents – your steed streaks through the air, soaring the length of the chamber, keeping close to the rafters and out of reach of the exploding bombs.

"Yippee-ki-yay!" you holler in exhilaration, but the rest of your exclamation is swallowed by the noise of the cacophonous detonations.

You can see a pair of finely-carved doors ahead of you, at the top of a wooden staircase.

Comet sets you down at the top of the stairs and you dismount, patting the reindeer's neck by way of a thank you, before passing through the double doors and entering what can only be the centre of operations here.

Turn to **485**.

380

Hearing a sudden snarl, you look up to see the driver leaving his seat at the front of the sleigh, as he scrambles over the piles of sacks in an attempt to get his filthy claws on you.

Make a note that your opponent has the initiative in the forthcoming battle and turn to **131**.

381

Back in the courtyard of the frozen castle, where do you want to go now?

The south-east tower?	Turn to **148**.
The south-west tower?	Turn to **89**.
The north-east tower?	Turn to **205**.
The north-west tower?	Turn to **34**.
The central keep?	Turn to **424**.

However, if you want to leave the castle, turn to **361**.

382

The metal drainpipe is freezing to the touch, but, despite this, you grab hold and use it to scale the side of the building, as you head for the roof. Higher and higher you climb into the snowy night.

Take an Endurance test. If you pass the test, turn to **48**, but if you fail the test, turn to **402**.

383

With the diabolical host distracted, it's time to end this.

To put it simply, stop the devil and save Christmas! But how do you intend to do that?

If you have a Mistletoe Spear, you will have a number associated with the artefact; turn to that section now. If not, turn to **61**.

384

It is bitterly cold and, despite pulling the collar of your dressing-gown up against the wind, soon your teeth are chattering and your whole body is shivering.

(Deduct 2 *Endurance* points, 1 *Agility* point, and 1 *Combat* point.)

If you are still alive, record the code word *Kold* on your Adventure Sheet before turning to **414**.

385

Reluctantly taking off the scarf that has been helping keep you warm this bitter winter night, you dangle it in front of the monstrous feline. The cat pounces, snatching the scarf from your grasp, and starts to roll around in the snow, suddenly as playful as a kitten.

While the cat is distracted, pulling the knitted strands of the scarf apart, what do you want to do?

Attack the animal?	Turn to **77**.
Run away?	Turn to **405**.

386

"If you've been naughty or if you've been nice,
With birch and with trap, I'll still strike you twice!"

And with that the Christmas Devil attacks! (In this battle, Krampus has the initiative.)

KRAMPUS	COMBAT 8	ENDURANCE 10

If Krampus wins a Combat Round, roll one die (or pick a card). If the number rolled is odd (or the card is red), he strikes you with his birch-whip (lose 2 *Endurance* points). If the number rolled is even (or the card is black), he catches you in the jaws of his man-trap (lose 2 *Endurance* points and reduce your *Combat* score by 1 point for the next Combat Round).

If you manage to win 3 Combat Rounds, or you reduce Krampus's *Endurance* score to 6 points or below, turn to **403** at once. If you do not manage either feat, the Christmas Devil will win this fight and your adventure will be over.

387

Ducking and diving, twisting and turning, you not only manage to keep up with your quarry, you actually catch them up. But as the cloaked figure turns to face you, you only then realise a thick mist has descended over the frozen river and you have left the huddle of stalls and temporary structures that make up the fair.

The looming figure is only a few strides away from you, but you can see nothing through the impenetrable shadows of its hood, apart from the suggestion of a scraggly beard and the points of a pair of curling horns. Precisely what is it that you have pursued across the ice?

A sudden sharp crack echoes across the surface of the frozen river and you feel the ice give. Your prey has tricked you, leading you out to the middle of the river where the ice is thinner. Warily, you take a step backwards but the ice fractures again as you do so.

If you want to see whether the universe thinks you've been *Naughty or Nice*, cross off one use and turn to **329**. If you do not want to invoke that power at the moment, turn to **349**.

388

Whirling the Ice Sword about you in a figure of eight pattern, you prepare to meet the Snowmen's icicle claws with the frozen blade. (In this battle, the Snowmen have the initiative, but you can fight them one at a time.)

	COMBAT	ENDURANCE
First SNOWMAN	6	7
Second SNOWMAN	7	7
Third SNOWMAN	6	6

If you manage to put an end to all three of the abominable Snowmen, turn to **408**.

389

Some demonstrate neat, careful penmanship, written in blue ink on headed notepaper, while others are barely more than notes scribbled in coloured crayon on any scrap of paper that came to hand at the time.

But what the letters all have in common is hope – the hope that Father Christmas will bring their authors the presents they really want this year – and that fills you with both the feeling that there will be a positive outcome to the night's proceedings, and a renewed determination to save Santa.

(You now have one extra use of *The Pen is Mightier* special ability; record this on your Adventure Sheet.)

Now turn to **479.**

390

The robot no longer a threat, you open the door it was guarding and step through.

Turn to **492**.

391

"Looks like you're getting ready for a right royal feast," you remark, as one of the trolls walks past the cage carrying a string of smoked sausages.

"Oh yes," says the Sausage-Swiper. "We won't have eaten so well since last Christmas."

"Well it won't be a real festive feast unless you've got something to drink. Here," you say, opening the bundle of good things La Befana gave you and taking out the Bottle of Schnapps, "have this on me. Think of it as an early Christmas present."

"That's very kind, I'm sure," says another of the trolls, who is chewing on a tallow candle, and takes the bottle from you.

The trolls stop what they are doing and share out the schnapps between them, forgetting that they are supposed to be laying the table for supper. They down glass after glass of the sharp, sweet spirit – even Mama Gryla joins in with their carousing – and soon the bottle is empty and your captors have all fallen asleep, having drunk themselves into a stupor.

(Cross the Bottle of Schnapps off your Adventure Sheet.)

The troll in charge of the keys has collapsed almost within reach. Through the bars of the cage you manage to pick up a twig from the unswept floor of the cave, and using this, you try to free the iron ring holding the keys from the hook on his belt.

Take an Agility test; if you pass the test, turn to **431**, but if you fail the test, turn to **411**.

392

Another room, another two very similar doors, and another question. This one reads:

What is myrrh anyway?

Which of the following options will you go with?

'An incense that gives off a bitter-smelling smoke'?	Turn to **416**.
'An incense that gives off a sweet-smelling smoke'?	Turn to **18**.

393

You take off for the shore, but immediately the thing that's under the ice – whatever it is – starts moving through the water with graceful speed.

Suddenly the *chung-chung* of a shockwave echoes across the lake, and the ice only a few stride-lengths ahead of you fractures, as a tangle of tentacles bursts through from beneath. And then the elongated, purple, squid-like arms are reaching for you, and you are forced to take evasive action.

Take an Agility test. If you pass the test, turn to **294**, if you fail the test, turn to **334**.

394

The walls of the room are covered with shelves, from floor to ceiling, and these shelves are crammed full of dolls and cuddly toys, ready to be sent out to children all over the world. There are even boxes on the floor filled with ragdolls and stuffed animals. The air is filled with a fine haze of lint and stuffing fibres, which makes you sneeze.

On the other side of the room is another door, leading onwards, but as you start to make your way towards it, a cardboard box sealed with tape suddenly starts to move, and you hear a deep growling coming from within it.

You are only half way across the large room when the box tips over and something tears its way out. You see instantly that it is a teddy bear, but it is almost as tall as you are, can move of its own volition, and has steel-sharp claws as well as a mouth crammed with needle-like teeth. And it is blocking your path to the other door.

The stuffed bear growls again and starts to move towards you.

What do you want to do? Will you:

Use the *Naughty or Nice* special ability (if you still can)?	Turn to **321**.
Use *The Pen is Mightier* special ability (if you still can)?	Turn to **261**.
Prepare to defend yourself against the malign teddy bear?	Turn to **281**.

395

The tree is decorated with tinsel and glittering baubles that reflect the twinkling colours of the fairy lights. Even though you only have to wait until the morning to open the presents lying beneath it, the temptation to take a sneaky peek at them now is almost overwhelming.

If you want to give in to temptation and start unwrapping the gifts, turn to **415**. If you would prefer to fight temptation and leave the sitting room through the door that leads to the kitchen, turn to **5**.

396

You snap off part of a gingerbread bench standing under the eaves, storing the crumbly cake in one of your capacious dressing-gown pockets.

Add 2 Meals to your Adventure Sheet and write down the code word *Krumbly*.

What do you want to do now? If you want to see if you can enter the cottage, turn to **366**. If you decide it's time for you to be on your way again, turn to **213**.

397

Incredibly, you make it to the top of the tower and finally haul yourself over the window ledge, dropping down into the chamber beyond.

You are surprised to see that the evergreens cover the inside of the building as well. Moonlight enters the chamber through a stained glass window depicting a sprig of mistletoe, and by the light cast by the silvery orb you see three stone tumblers set into the floor.

As you are pondering what they could be for, two elfin figures emerge from the plants covering the walls. They are clearly both female, but they are also quite clearly formed from the plants – one of holly and one of ivy.

"Greetings, stranger," says Holly. "See the tumblers in the floor?" You nod. "If the treasure you would find, solve the riddle written here."

"Once the stones are all aligned, you will win the white-wood spear," Ivy concludes.

The twin plant-people point at a spot on the wall where the moonlight picks out twelve words carved into the stone.

If you want to attempt to solve the riddle, turn to **477**. If you would rather leave the tower, the same way you climbed up, turn to **381**. If you want to attack the evergreens, in the hope of forcing them to tell you the answer to the riddle themselves, turn to **417**.

398

You decide that your only chance of escaping the clockwork bombs is to make a break for it, bounding right through the middle of the advancing devices. But as you do so, the first of them detonates, initiating a chain reaction.

Roll one die and add 2. Deduct this many *Endurance* points. (Alternatively, pick a card and deduct its face value from your *Endurance* score, unless it is 9 or above, or a picture card, in which case deduct 8 points from your *Endurance* score.)

If you have lost a total of 5 *Endurance* points or more, you must also deduct 1 point from your *Agility* score, and if you have lost a total of 7 *Endurance* points or more, also deduct 1 point from your *Combat* score.

If you are still alive, turn to **121**.

399

"Krampus has the key," the Chief Elf, whose name is Jingle, says dejectedly.

"But I think I know where a spare is kept," says Sugarplum.

"Where?" you ask excitedly.

"Mrs Christmas keeps one in the pocket of her apron."

"And where might I find Mrs Christmas?" you ask.

"In her pantry, past the kitchens," says Jingle.

"And where are the kitchens?"

"At the other end of that corridor," the Chief Elf says, pointing through the grim doorway by which you entered the dungeon cell.

If you ever find yourself reading a section that begins *'Reaching the far side of the kitchen…'* you may look for Mrs Christmas's pantry by deducting 50 from the section number and turning to this section instead.

But for the time being, you have no choice but to leave the imprisoned Elves where they are, and make your way along the corridor towards the kitchens.

Turn to **362**.

400

"You have my book!" Father Christmas suddenly calls out in excitement. "Do you happen to have a bell and a candle as well?"

If you have a Bell and a Candle, as well as the book, turn to **80**. If not, you are going to have to fight the devil in order to rescue Father Christmas – turn to **74**.

401

Warily, you step out onto the ice bridge, but when you see that it can hold your weight quite happily, you hurry across it, pass beneath the frozen gatehouse, and enter a wide courtyard.

The moon shines brightly overhead, bathing the fortress in its monochrome light. You can see now that not all of the castle is made of ice; the walls, and the towers that sit at the four corners where the walls meet, are all constructed from stone. However, the central keep does indeed appear to have been put together from great blocks of ice.

The place is eerily silent – as quiet as the grave, in fact – but you are not alone here; the courtyard is full of the most intricate ice sculptures of people, but they are contorted into all manner of agonised shapes, with tortured expressions frozen on their faces. Their presence here is unnervingly chilling.

You have two options open to you: you can either explore the frozen castle, or leave. If you want to explore, where do you want to go first?

The south-east tower? Turn to **148**.

The south-west tower? Turn to **89**.

The north-east tower? Turn to **205**.

The north-west tower? Turn to **34**.

The central keep? Turn to **424**.

If you would rather leave, without exploring the castle first, turn to **421**.

402

You are up to the second storey, and almost within reach of the roof, when your grip on the icy drainpipe slips. Your aching arms too tired to hang on any longer, you fall from the side of the house.

If you want to use your *Naughty or Nice* special ability, turn to **472**. If not, turn to **442**.

403

In his fury Krampus stamps his single cloven hoof down hard. In response, the ground suddenly and dramatically splits apart, and an ever-widening fissure zigzags towards you, and you are struck by a gust of hot air rising from the infernal pit beneath, as snow turns to steam around it.

Take an Agility test. If you pass the test, turn to **114**. If you fail the test, turn to **433**.

404

(Record the code word *Kurious* on your Adventure Sheet.)

Entering the keep through a grandly-sculpted entrance, you proceed to explore a maze of frozen halls and frost-rimed rooms – all of them empty, all of them eerily quiet – until, at the end of an icy passageway, you see a grand ante-chamber with a set of glacial double doors, currently closed to the room beyond. Standing before them are two more of the ice sculptures, only these have been carved in the shape of powerful figures holding polearms.

If you have the Box of Delights, turn to **374**. If not, turn to **312**.

405

You turn tail and run, half expecting the cat to come after you at any moment.

Turn to **453**.

406

"That's a relief," says the witch. "For a moment there I thought you were an agent of that devil Krampus, the goat-leggéd one. Are you a friend of Father Christmas then?"

"Are you?" you counter.

"But of course," she replies, back on the defensive. "After all, I help make deliveries to the children of Italy," she explains, "for I am La Befana, the Christmas Witch."

"Then maybe you can help me," you go on, opening up to her as you describe the course of events that have brought you to her gingerbread cottage on this cold Christmas Eve. "Father Christmas is in grave danger."

"I knew it! He must have been abducted by that devil Krampus!" she butts in. "The demon's agents are everywhere."

She leans in close, lowering her voice, as if afraid that even the spiders in their webs in the rafters might be among Krampus's spies.

"Do you know where Krampus has taken him?"

Unfortunately you don't.

"We cannot delay then. If we travel separately, we might have a better chance of finding them, but then again, two against one is better odds, if we can track them down. What do you think?"

How will you answer?

"Let's split up." Turn to **438**.

"Let's look for them together." Turn to **458**.

407

It is time you were on your way. As you leave the Punch and Judy showman under the bridge, he calls out to you one last time. "Beware, the wolves are running, and the black goat too."

The Punch and Judy Man's strange warning echoing through your head, you make for the edge of the frost fair and the frozen riverbank...

...and then suddenly you feel carpet through the soles of your slippers again, and find yourself back in the night-dark sitting room.

Turn to **219**.

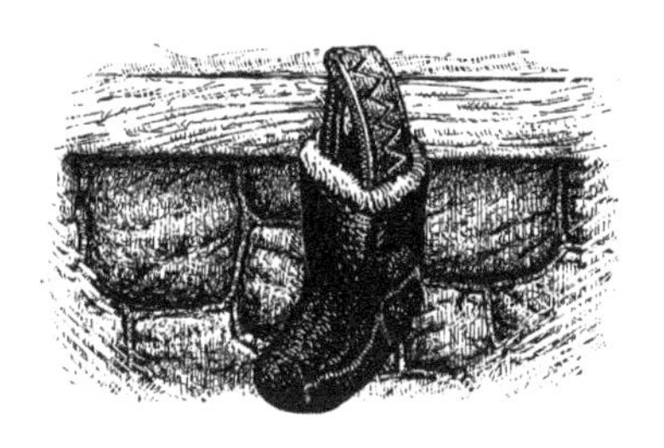

408

Having reduced the snowmen to piles of crumbling ice crystals, with the sword indisputably in your possession now, you go to leave the chamber. But as you do so, you suddenly hear a voice inside your head, as sharp and clear as ice.

My name is Frostbite, the voice says, *and I am anathema to all demonkind.*

Record the Ice Sword on your Adventure Sheet. Whenever you use Frostbite in battle against an imp, a devil, or a demon, you may add 2 points when calculating your *Combat Rating*, and any successful hit you deliver with the sword will cause 1 additional point of damage.

Now turn to **363**.

409

With your hands stuffed inside the pockets of your dressing-gown, to keep them warm, you realise that you are absent-mindedly stroking the smooth wood of the box… which gives you an idea!

If you know what you need to do to go swift, and you want to draw on the box's power at this juncture, do it now. If you don't know, or you don't want to speed up your journey, turn to **280**.

410

It's no good – there just isn't the strength left in your legs to carry you to safety. The walls grind inexorably together, and before you can reach the far door you are crushed between them like a bug.

Your adventure is over.

The End

411

You manage to free the key-ring from the troll's belt, but in your hurry to retrieve them, you knock them against the bars of the cage, stirring the sleeping trolls.

"What's going on?" asks a troll who is as thin as the licked spoon he holds in one hand.

You're never going to get a better opportunity than this, so, as your captors come to their senses again, you unlock the cage and burst out of it, running for the round door.

Turn to **199**.

412

Choosing your moment, you sprint towards the swinging Christmas bells.

Take an Agility test. If you pass the test, turn to **292**, but if you fail the test, turn to **272**.

413

The imposter-Elves suddenly scatter as a phalanx of wind-up toys whirrs towards your position. They look like a cartoonist's interpretation of a bomb – each having a spherical black body, with a sparking fuse sticking out of the top, and a gleeful, painted-on face – and they advance with clumping steps.

And then you see the fuse on each is rapidly burning down and you come to the horrible realisation that they really are bombs, and they are about to explode!

But surely you can outrun them! Turning round, you see that you are surrounded by the self-propelled explosive devices, and they are steadily closing in, with you their intended target.

If you have the word code word *Komet* recorded on your Adventure Sheet, turn to **379**. If not, turn to **398**.

414

Although you are aware of your immediate location, you have no idea where that is in relation to your home. The night's sky thick with wintry clouds, you cannot even locate north, but not knowing what else to do, you set off regardless, trudging through the snow. And then a light appears through the darkness.

Drawn to the light like a moth to a candle-flame, you soon find yourself before a single-storey hovel. Thick smoke rises from a stone-built chimney, but the rest of the building is constructed from wood, with a layer of haphazard thatch on the roof.

Do you want to knock on the door, in the hope of finding shelter from the night and the cold (turn to **4**), or would you rather keep trudging through the snow, heading in what you think is roughly the same direction as the sleigh went (turn to **444**)?

415

Three presents, in their gaudy wrapping paper and tied with ostentatious ribbons, attract your attention. Which one do you want to open first?

A small, soft parcel wrapped in silver snowflake paper?	Turn to **435**.
A long present wrapped in gold metallic gift wrap?	Turn to **455**.
A large box, wrapped in black flock paper bearing a gift tag addressed to you?	Turn to **475**.

419

imagined the day would come when you would
ıt off a baker's dozen of gingerbread men!

t to employ *The Pen is Mightier* special ability, turn
ou want to risk using your *Naughty or Nice* special
n to **107**. If you do not want to use either of your
lities at this time, or they are no longer available to
o **494**.

420

bout inside the basket, you nonetheless get the sense
are being carried up onto the roof of your house,
ne become aware of the snorting, and musky animal
arge cervidae.

uctor shrugs the basket from its shoulders and tosses
a large pile of sacks. You start to suspect that you are
board a huge sleigh!

sport rocks as the giant climbs aboard, you hear the
ack of a whip, and feel a jolt as the sleigh takes off,
mach lurching as the vehicle hurtles skyward.

g that your abductor will be preoccupied with driving
gh, you make a bid for freedom. Poking your fingers
the gaps between the woven lengths of willow, you
to jiggle the toggle keeping the basket shut free
p the lid open. Clouds, heavy with snow, rush past
ad, beneath a midnight blue velvet sky, scattered with
n twinkling diamond stars.

ng out of the basket you have your suspicions
ned; you have been tossed into the back of a sleigh piled
ith sacks. And one of those sacks, which is larger than
t, is wriggling as whoever – or whatever! – is inside it,
les to get free.

416

Pulling open the door, you confidently step through, and let it slam shut again behind you.

Turn to **492**.

417

Fixing you with glowing green eyes, the elemental entities begin to chant:

"The holly and the ivy,
Forever evergreen,
Should anyone ever threaten them,
They'll never again be seen!"

As they chant, the knotted vines of ivy and boughs of holly pull free of the walls and envelope you in their prickly and allergy-inducing foliage, and no matter how hard you fight against them, you cannot prevail. The spikes of the holly leaves tear your skin open, and the ivy tightens around your neck until you can no longer breathe.

You end your adventure, throttled by a pair of plants.

The End

You are standing at the entrance to a vast chamber that is full of noise, machinery and Elves. At least you take them for Elves, until you focus on their hideous features and horrible leering demonic sneers.

The hub of Father Christmas's toy factory is one vast production line. Miles and miles of clanking wooden conveyor belts criss-cross the vaulted space, which is also decorated with a veritable forest of Christmas trees, and which in turn are adorned with miles of tinsel and a profusion of blown-glass baubles.

The scale of the operation takes your breath away; everywhere you look there are mountains of presents, tied with ribbon. The horrible impish creatures working at the production line are adding to the stacks all the time, although you're not sure the toys they are making are on anyone's Christmas list this year. There are grim-faced dolls wielding bloody axes, headless teddy bears, and clockwork creations with snapping gin-trap jaws.

Over the clattering of the assembly line, you can hear the cackling cacophony of the imps' singing.

"On the first day of Christmas, Lord Krampus made for me,
Mass carnage and cruel devilry.
On the second day of Christmas, Lord Krampus made for me,
Two pudding bombs, and mass carnage and cruel devilry."

And then suddenly one of the horrors catches sight of you. At the imp's shout of surprise, several of the Elf-imposters break off from what they are doing and advance towards you, improvised weapons in hand.

You have attracted the attention of Krampus's little helpers but how do you want to respond?

Prepare to face them in battle?	Turn to **463**.
Try to run away?	Turn to **434**.
Use the Box of Delights (if you can)?	Turn to **267**.

You never
have to fig

If you war
to **359**. If y
ability, tur
special abi
you, turn

Thrown a
that you
and in tir
scent, of

Your abd
it among
now on

The tran
sharp cr
your sto

Realisin
the slei
through
manage
and po
overhe
a milli

Crawli
confirn
high w
the res
strugg

If you want to untie the knotted cord that is keeping the sack closed, turn to **144**. If you would rather not risk unleashing what might be lurking within, turn to **380.**

421

Leaving the castle behind, you set off north again, tramping through the snow, but the relentless, bitter cold seeps into your very bones.

(Deduct 2 *Endurance* points, 1 *Agility* point, and 1 *Combat* point.)

If you haven't died from hypothermia yet, turn to **244**.

422

As you lie there in the snow, staring up at the starless sky, you hear the jingle of bells, the crack of a whip, and something suddenly takes off from the roof of your house. Rocketing into the sky, as fast as a comet, it sends a cascade of snow tumbling from the roof tiles.

As it rapidly disappears into the darkness – a silvery substance, like frost on snow, trickling from the sleigh's runners as it departs – you notice something drifting down to the ground amidst the swirling snowflakes.

Reaching out a cautious hand and plucking the curl of parchment from the air, you hold it in front of your nose. Written on it, in glittering black ink, in an ornate gothic hand is:

Help Me!
F. C.

You stare at the piece of parchment incredulously. Could it really be…?

But if it is, how are you supposed to help him now that his favoured mode of transport has already left?

If you are in possession of the Box of Delights, turn to **136**. If not, turn to **62**.

423

(Cross off one use of the *Naughty or Nice* special ability.)

A booming voice suddenly cuts through the night, as it carries through the forest: "Here, kitty-kitty! Come to Mama!"

The cat freezes.

The trees part and a colossal humanoid figure appears. It is an ugly, ill-formed woman, a hideous giantess, her lumpen features covered with hair-sprouting warts.

"There you are, you naughty kitty," the giantess says. "Come to Mama Gryla."

As she reaches for the cat, the beast takes off, fast as a scalded cat, and vanishes among the pines. But then Mama Gryla catches sight of you.

"What have we here?" she mutters.

Paralysed with fear, you are unable to resist as the giantess reaches down and picks you up in one huge gnarled hand.

"Looks like supper to me."

Turn to **234**.

424

You make your way towards the entrance to the ice-locked keep.

If you have the code word *Kurious* written on your Adventure Sheet, turn to **361**. If not, turn to **404**.

425

You set to work, with Santa's little helpers looking on, and in no time at all you hear a click and the cage door swings open.

Turn to **23**.

426

Breaking off a piece of gingerbread from the low-hanging eaves, you take a bite. It is crumbly, and sweet, but with a spicy aftertaste. In fact, it is delicious and you quickly finish off the sample! (Gain 2 *Endurance* points.)

If you want to break off some more of the gingerbread to save for later, turn to **396**.

If not, do you want to see if you can enter the cottage (turn to **366**), or will you be on your way now (turn to **213**)?

427

"This," says the Punch and Judy Man, "is my Box of Delights."

He hands it to you. It appears to be quite unremarkable; it is made from polished pear wood and has a small brass button on the lid.

"There are two things you must know about the Box." He places a callused finger on top of the brass button. "If you push it to the right you can go small, and if you press it to the left you can go swift."

If you are ever given the option of using the Box of Delights to go swift, add 20 to the section you are reading at the time and turn to that new section.

If you are ever given the option of using the Box of Delights to go small, deduct 20 from the section you are reading and turn to this new section to continue your adventure.

But for now, record the Box of Delights in the Equipment box on your Adventure Sheet, making a note that you may only use it three times before expending all of its power, and then turn to **407**.

428

(Cross off one use of *The Pen is Mightier* special ability.)

Hearing a sudden sharp crack come from above, you look up as one of the hanging icicle-stalactites breaks away from the roof of the cave and drops like a spear towards you. You dodge out of the way, just in time, but only just, the icicle hitting the sword and smashing it from your grasp.

There are several more splintering cracks, and more of the icicles come down, obliterating the half-formed snowmen.

Fearing that the whole roof could come down at any moment, you sprint for the far side of the cave.

Turn to **363**.

429

Pushing the button to the left, you hurtle into the snow-swept sky. You soar over the lake and the wintry wonderland until the gatehouse of the frost-rimed castle comes into view, and you touch down on *terra firma* once more.

Turn to **446**.

430

Mrs Christmas's captor dealt with, you turn your attention to the old lady, hastily untying her.

"Thank you, my dear," Mrs Christmas says, as soon as you remove the gag from her mouth. "For a moment there, I really thought I was done for."

"What happened?" you ask, as you set to work loosening the

416

Pulling open the door, you confidently step through, and let it slam shut again behind you.

Turn to **492**.

417

Fixing you with glowing green eyes, the elemental entities begin to chant:

"The holly and the ivy,
Forever evergreen,
Should anyone ever threaten them,
They'll never again be seen!"

As they chant, the knotted vines of ivy and boughs of holly pull free of the walls and envelope you in their prickly and allergy-inducing foliage, and no matter how hard you fight against them, you cannot prevail. The spikes of the holly leaves tear your skin open, and the ivy tightens around your neck until you can no longer breathe.

You end your adventure, throttled by a pair of plants.

The End

418

You are standing at the entrance to a vast chamber that is full of noise, machinery and Elves. At least you take them for Elves, until you focus on their hideous features and horrible leering demonic sneers.

The hub of Father Christmas's toy factory is one vast production line. Miles and miles of clanking wooden conveyor belts criss-cross the vaulted space, which is also decorated with a veritable forest of Christmas trees, and which in turn are adorned with miles of tinsel and a profusion of blown-glass baubles.

The scale of the operation takes your breath away; everywhere you look there are mountains of presents, tied with ribbon. The horrible impish creatures working at the production line are adding to the stacks all the time, although you're not sure the toys they are making are on anyone's Christmas list this year. There are grim-faced dolls wielding bloody axes, headless teddy bears, and clockwork creations with snapping gin-trap jaws.

Over the clattering of the assembly line, you can hear the cackling cacophony of the imps' singing.

"On the first day of Christmas, Lord Krampus made for me,
Mass carnage and cruel devilry.
On the second day of Christmas, Lord Krampus made for me,
Two pudding bombs, and mass carnage and cruel devilry."

And then suddenly one of the horrors catches sight of you. At the imp's shout of surprise, several of the Elf-imposters break off from what they are doing and advance towards you, improvised weapons in hand.

You have attracted the attention of Krampus's little helpers but how do you want to respond?

Prepare to face them in battle? Turn to **463**.

Try to run away? Turn to **434**.

Use the Box of Delights (if you can)? Turn to **267**.

419

You never imagined the day would come when you would have to fight off a baker's dozen of gingerbread men!

If you want to employ *The Pen is Mightier* special ability, turn to **359**. If you want to risk using your *Naughty or Nice* special ability, turn to **107**. If you do not want to use either of your special abilities at this time, or they are no longer available to you, turn to **494**.

420

Thrown about inside the basket, you nonetheless get the sense that you are being carried up onto the roof of your house, and in time become aware of the snorting, and musky animal scent, of large cervidae.

Your abductor shrugs the basket from its shoulders and tosses it among a large pile of sacks. You start to suspect that you are now on board a huge sleigh!

The transport rocks as the giant climbs aboard, you hear the sharp crack of a whip, and feel a jolt as the sleigh takes off, your stomach lurching as the vehicle hurtles skyward.

Realising that your abductor will be preoccupied with driving the sleigh, you make a bid for freedom. Poking your fingers through the gaps between the woven lengths of willow, you manage to jiggle the toggle keeping the basket shut free and pop the lid open. Clouds, heavy with snow, rush past overhead, beneath a midnight blue velvet sky, scattered with a million twinkling diamond stars.

Crawling out of the basket you have your suspicions confirmed; you have been tossed into the back of a sleigh piled high with sacks. And one of those sacks, which is larger than the rest, is wriggling as whoever – or whatever! – is inside it, struggles to get free.

ropes binding her to the rocking chair.

"It was that Krampus, the fiend, and after we've provided him with a roof over his head these last I don't know how many centuries. But his discontentment must have been brewing a long time. When the attack came it all happened so quickly I didn't know what was going on. He waited until my husband had gone out on his rounds, of course. I only pray Jingle, Sugarplum and the others are all right. And I hate to think how his goblins might have adulterated my recipes!"

"I know where Santa's little helpers are," you tell the concerned old lady. "Krampus has them locked up in his old cell. I came here to find the means to let them out."

"Then you'll be needing this," says Mrs Christmas, pulling a large iron key from a pocket in her apron.

With the cell key in your possession, you make for the door out of the pantry again.

"Mind how you go!" Mrs Christmas calls after you, as you leave.

Keeping to the shadows at the edge of the kitchen, you go back out the way you first came in and, making your way back down the corridor, return to the chamber in which the Elves have been imprisoned.

Jingle, Sugarplum and the others are delighted, if amazed, to see you, the look on their beaming faces, as you fit the heavy iron key into the lock on the cage door, speaking volumes. And then you hear a click and the cage opens.

Turn to **23.**

431

You manage to retrieve the keys and let yourself out of the cage, without disturbing the sleeping trolls or their giantess mother. As you creep between the snoring brothers, you see a number of items that you are tempted to take with you: a bell, a lantern, and a pair of ice picks. (If you want to take any of the items, add them to the Equipment box on your Adventure Sheet.)

Finally making it to the door, you quietly let yourself out. Pulling your dressing-gown tight about you, you set off again through the night-shrouded forest.

Turn to **473**.

432

Opening the door labelled 'TOYS', you step through and find yourself in a large room, lit by a single lantern hanging from the middle of the ceiling.

Roll one die (or pick a card). If the number rolled is odd (or the card is red), turn to **394**. If the number rolled is even (or the card is black), turn to **293**.

433

If you want to use your *Naughty or Nice* special ability, and you still can, cross off one use and turn to **114**. If not, turn to **309**.

434

Surrounded by the impish workers, in a bid to escape them, you scramble onto a juddering conveyor belt. But as you start to ride the rattling track through the factory, an ugly green-skinned creature, with large pointed ears, wild yellow eyes, too many teeth – and wearing a tiny Santa suit – drops onto the conveyor in front of you from another that swings past overhead.

Giggling hysterically, the Gremlin goes for you.

If you want to use *The Pen is Mightier* special ability, and you still can, cross off one use and turn to **357**. If not, turn to **338**.

435

Tearing open the parcel, you are disappointed to find a woolly hat, gloves and a scarf inside. But you tuck them inside your dressing gown nonetheless.

(Record the code word *Kosy* on your Adventure Sheet.)

Now do you want to:

Open the long, gold-wrapped present?	Turn to **455**.
Open the large, black-wrapped present?	Turn to **475**.
Leave the sitting room for the kitchen?	Turn to **5**.

436

As soon as you are through the door, it slams shut behind you. You are in another small room with two more near-identical doors in front of you, but this time, the question painted on the facing wall reads:

What are the four weeks leading up to Christmas called?

One word is painted on each of the doors in front of you, but which one will you choose to walk through?

'Advent'?	Turn to **456**.
'Yuletide?	Turn to **108**.

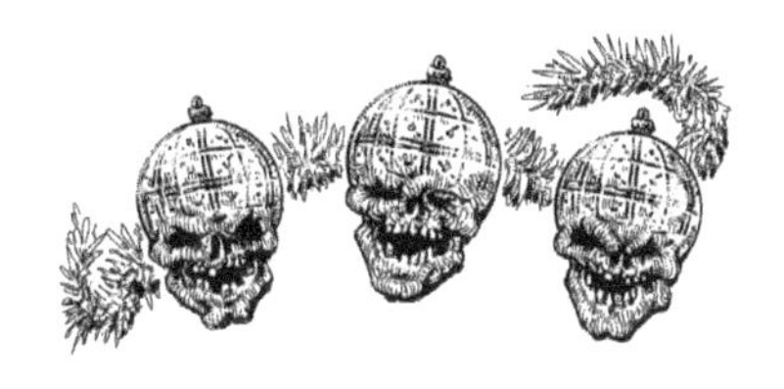

437

With a furious flapping of wings, something suddenly flies out of the chimney and into the office, showering the work stations with soot.

The thing looks like a winged puppet – as of an angel, or the fairy you might expect to see perched on top of a Christmas tree. Underneath all the soot you are able to make out a filthy dress, while its oversized head is fashioned from cracked china. Glass eyes roll in their sockets until they finally come to rest on you. The puppet's articulated jaw clacks open and gives voice to a high-pitched giggle that is like the tinkling of a musical box.

It is the Perchta – an ally of the Christmas Devil Krampus!

Giggling insanely, the animated puppet reaches for you with twitching wooden fingers.

If you want to use *The Pen is Mightier* special ability, and you still can, cross off one use and turn to **82**. If not, turn to **30**.

438

"Good idea," says the witch, "but before you set off again, let me provide you with some vittals for the journey."

From her larder, she puts together a bundle, wrapped up in a muslin cloth, containing hard cheese, dried figs, and a stoppered bottle of schnapps.

The food is enough for 2 Meals. The Bottle of Schnapps contains four measures, with each measure restoring 3 *Endurance* points. However, if you drink more than one measure in one go, you must also reduce your *Combat* score by 1 point for every measure over the initial one that you drink, until after your next battle. (For example, if you drank two measures in one go, you would have to temporarily reduce your *Combat* score by 1 point, but if you drank three measures in one go, you would have to reduce your *Combat* score by 2 points, and so on.)

You and La Befana leave the gingerbread cottage together, but while the witch rides her broomstick into the sky, you set off on foot, trudging north through the forest, following the crone's directions.

Record the code word *Kind* on your Adventure Sheet and then turn to **213**.

439

The creatures soaring and swooping overhead cackle with sinister glee as they sweep through the air, apparently unhindered by gravity.

If you have the code word *Kruel* written on your Adventure Sheet, turn to **335**.

If not, and you have the code word *Kind* recorded on your Adventure Sheet, turn to **352**. Otherwise, turn to **335** anyway.

440

Reaching the door at the other end of the corridor of so-called 'GAMES' – your salvation! – you are relieved to find that it is unlocked and let yourself out.

Turn to **492**.

441

Opening the door – it is not locked – you enter what is patently a prison cell. Only a few paces from the entrance, the chamber is bisected by a wall of bars, in the middle of which is a cage door.

Packed in behind the bars are dozens and dozens of forlorn-looking figures. While they are all clearly adults, they are all shorter than you, and from their garish, pied clothes and noticeably pointed ears, you can only assume that they are Santa's helpers, the Elves you would expect to find slaving away in his workshop.

Upon catching sight of you, their changing expressions run the whole gamut of emotions, from anxious, to bewildered, to hopeful, as they realise that you are not the one who imprisoned them here, but that you might actually be their salvation!

"Who are you?" asks a female Elf wearing purple clothes, and red curly-toed shoes.

You tell her your name and, as the Elves press you for more information, asking how you came to be here, you end up relating the details of your journey through the arctic wilderness to the home of Father Christmas.

In return they tell you how Krampus and his imps took them by surprise, rounding them up and imprisoning them in the very cell that had been the Christmas Devil's home for the last two millennia.

"Let us out and we will help you overcome the usurper and his imps, and put them back where they belong," the female Elf, whose name is Sugarplum, says with grim resolution.

This sounds like a much better plan than taking on the Christmas Devil by yourself. However, the cell is locked and there is no sign of a key.

If you have a set of Lockpicks or a Skeleton Key, turn to **425**. If not, turn to **399**.

442

You land heavily on your back outside the back door.

Roll one die and add 1. Deduct this many *Endurance* points. (Alternatively, pick a card and deduct its face value from your *Endurance* score, unless it is 8 or above or a picture card, in which case deduct 7 points from your *Endurance* score.)

If you survive the fall, turn to **422**. If not, your adventure ends here…

443

Dreading to think what might happen if you moved even an inch, you freeze, desperately hoping that the monster – whatever it is – will lose interest and simply go away, while the enormous eye remains where it is, just under the ice, staring up at you.

If you want to use the *Naughty or Nice* special ability, and you still can, cross off one use and turn to **476**. If not, turn to **460.**

444

If you have the code word *Kold* written on your Adventure Sheet, turn to **464**. If not, turn to **484**.

445

Some demonstrate neat, careful penmanship, written in blue ink on headed notepaper, while others are barely more than notes scribbled in coloured crayon on any scrap of paper that came to hand at the time.

But what the letters all have in common is hope – the hope that Father Christmas will bring their authors the presents they really want this year – and that fills you with both the feeling that there will be a positive outcome to the night's proceedings, and a renewed determination to save Santa.

(You now have one extra use of *The Pen is Mightier* special ability; record this on your Adventure Sheet.)

As you read the children's letters, you become aware of a fluttering sound, coming from the stone-built fireplace. It sounds like something has got stuck up the chimney. Will you:

Go over to the fireplace and take a look? Turn to **479**.

Take a closer look at the large leather-bound book? Turn to **482**.

Leave the office and continue your search for Father Christmas? Turn to **66**.

446

You stand in the shadow of the craggy foothills of the mountain range. Rising from amidst the icy, snow-capped peaks is a colossal edifice that looks like it has been carved from ice, complete with sturdy towers and frost-rimed flying buttresses. The whole castle looks like it wouldn't be out of place as a decoration on an extremely grand Christmas cake.

Leading to a glacial gatehouse is a bridge of blemish-free ice that spans the deep crevasse that rings the fortress. As far as you can tell, there is no one about.

If you want to cross the ice bridge with the intention of entering the castle, turn to **401**. If you are uneasy about entering the edifice and would rather steer well clear, turn to **421**.

447

"Ah," the old man says, "I see that my Barney Dog has made friends with you at first sight. That's the time that likings are made."

There is a twinkle in the Punch and Judy Man's eyes, like that of stars on a clear night.

"Are you here to watch my puppet show?" he asks you,

and you have to confess that you are not. "Ah, I have other delights besides my show." He taps a little flat wooden box that is suddenly in his calloused hand. "Come, let me show you."

If you want to do as the old man bids, turn to **427**, but if not, turn to **407**.

448

As you push the button to the right, the Ice Sword slips from you grasp and lands in the snow covering the floor of the cave. Before you can pick it up again, you shrink in size until you are no taller than a fairy on top of a Christmas tree.

The lumbering snowmen are colossal giants now, but they are also much slower and clumsier than you, and it is easy to dash past them into the tunnel on the far side of the cave.

As you make your way along it, following its undulating path through the glacier, you soon return to your normal size, now that you are out of immediate danger. Eventually emerging on the far side of the glacier, you find yourself looking out across a vast ice-sheet, from the northern perimeter of the mountain pass.

And there, not half a league away, you see the flickering of candle-light coming from the windows of a vast structure of stone and wood. It must be Santa's workshop!

Turn to **100**.

449

Desperate to put as great a distance as you can between yourself and the wolves, you set off at a sprint.

Take an Endurance test. If you pass the test, turn to **469**, but if you fail the test, turn to **486**.

450

A shrill whistle suddenly cuts through the air and you realise the kettle Mrs Christmas has hung over her little fire is boiling… and that gives you an idea!

Ducking past the Candyman, you pull the kettle from its hook and hurl it at the artificially-flavoured freak. The Candyman is immediately drenched in boiling water and starts to dissolve.

"Melting!" it screams. "I'm melting!" But its shrill screams are soon silenced as the hard-boiled horror is reduced to a viscous puddle of sticky syrup that oozes across the floor in defeat.

Cross off one use of your special ability and turn to **430**.

451

"Looks like you're getting ready for a slap-up meal," you say to one of the trolls, as it walks past the cage, scraping the remains of some previous meal from the pot in its hands.

"Oh yes," says the Pot-Scraper. "We don't get to have human bean stew very often. It's our favourite!"

"Well, if you want my advice, if you really want to bring out of the flavour of the human bean, you should add some carrots to the broth, and I just so happen to have some here," you say, offering the troll the carrots that were supposed to have been for Santa's reindeer.

"Thank you kindly," says another of the trolls, who is carrying a bowl of what looks like yoghurt.

The Pot-Scraper takes the vegetables from you, chops them up, and adds them to contents of the cauldron bubbling away over the fire.

After a few minutes of stirring, the giantess draws a ladleful of the water from the pot and slurps the steaming stock.

"Mmm, delicious!" she announces. "Have you got anything else we can add?" she asks.

"As it happens, I have," you say, grabbing a smooth stone from the floor through the bars of the cage and holding it up. "This stone. Let me out of the cage and I'll help you prepare the tastiest stock you ever had."

"A stone?" laughs the giantess. "Pull the other one, it's got sleigh bells on it!"

"No, I'm serious," you say, bluffing, "but the only way you'll know is if you let me out of this cage."

Mama Gryla suffers a moment of indecision and then instructs the troll holding the keys to open the cage and let you out.

Do you want to make a break for it (turn to **199**), or do you want to draw out your ruse a little longer (turn to **88**)?

452

The imps carry you out through the stable doors again and, between them, drag you over the snow to the top of a snow-covered hill. The sight that greets you, has you looking on in horror and disbelief.

A diabolical sigil has been marked out in the snow with soot, comprising of a pentagram bound within a circle. At each of the five points of the demonic star there burns a brazier, fashioned from an upturned antlered skull atop a wooden pole.

But what is more horrible to your appalled gaze than the unholy symbol itself is the fact that a slightly overweight old man lies trussed up at its centre, and judging by his round belly, red coat and trousers, and white beard it can only be Father Christmas!

Standing at the bottom point of the inverted star is your nemesis, the one you have hunted for, far and wide this night, the hideous, horned, goat-leggéd Christmas Devil himself – Krampus!

Four crow-like figures, draped in tattered cloaks, stand behind the braziers that mark out the remaining four points of the pentagram, while more of the ragged figures whirl through the sky, black silhouettes against the coruscating Northern Lights.

The chanting voices of the figures drift to you over the snow, and although you cannot understand what they are saying, it nonetheless makes the hairs on the back of your neck stand on end. You can only assume that the devil and his servants are enacting a dark rite to break Santa's power, doubtless intending to usurp his position.

Turn to **481**.

453

As you continue to make your way through the pine trees, the ground starts to rise and becomes rocky underfoot. And then through the trees ahead of you, you see a flickering light coming from a small window at the entrance to a large cave. However, the entrance is blocked by a circular doorway that is twice as tall as you are.

Could this be the place you have been searching for?

Do you want to approach the entrance and knock on the door (turn to **75**), or do you want to keep trudging through the night-clad forest (turn to **473**)?

453

454

With a furious flapping of wings, something suddenly flies out of the chimney and into the office, showering the work stations with soot.

It's only a robin, but then the bird speaks! "Quick-quick!" it chirrups. "Come quick! Old Man Christmas need you!"

Urged on by the red-breast's urgent tweeting, you leave the office to continue your search.

Turn to **66.**

455

Undoing the red ribbon tied around the parcel, you cautiously start to unwrap it. You are surprised to find first a golden hilt and then a magnificent silver blade. It is a sword! But who could have put that under the tree? It's certainly not the most conventional of Christmas gifts.

(Record the Silver Sword on your Adventure Sheet and make a note that, if you use the sword in battle, you may add 1 point to your *Combat Rating*.)

As your marvel at the magnificent blade, your eyes fall on the large black-wrapped present.

If you want to open the present addressed to you, turn to **475**. If not, turn to **5**.

456

Another room, another two very similar doors, and another question. This one reads:

What is the name of Father Christmas's wife?

Which of the two options will you go with?

'Mary'?	Turn to **18**.
'Merry'?	Turn to **68**.

457

Krampus leans closer, his long pock-marked tongue writhing from his fanged mouth as if with a life of its own, and you almost retch as the devil's rancid breath comes at you in rancid gusts.

You cannot help but meet his horribly bulging yellow eyes and stare into the pinpricks of darkness that are the pupils within.

"I'll ask you just once – I'll not ask you twice –
Have you, my child, been naughty or nice?"

As you are struggling to resist the devil's hypnotic power, a rich warm voice reaches your ears.

"Do not fear, child," it says, "for I know where your name would appear in my great book, for you have a good heart and honourable intentions."

Father Christmas's encouragement is just what you need to break free of the hold Krampus has over you.

Cross off one use of the *Naughty or Nice* special ability and turn to **284**.

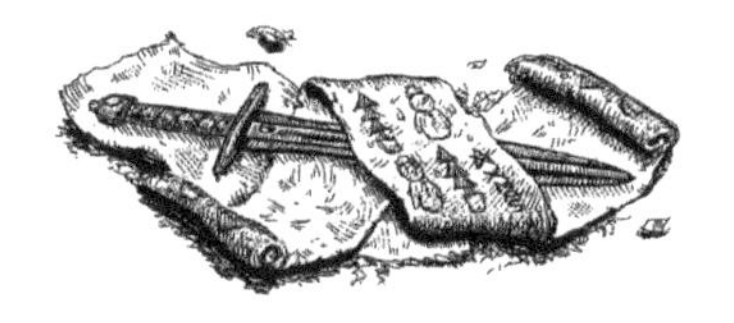

458

"That'll probably be for the best," says the witch.

(Record the code word *Kind* on your Adventure Sheet.)

The two of you leave the gingerbread cottage and, once outside, La Befana straddles her broomstick, encouraging you to climb on behind her.

"Hold on tight," she says, as the broomstick shoots up into the sky.

The clouds have cleared now, and by the light of the moon you can see the forest laid out beneath you. Beyond the trees lie the jagged teeth of the mountain range, but as you rise higher, buffeted by the cold wind, you can just make out a bleak white icefield beyond it. And there, in that frozen wilderness, you can see the warm orange glow of distant lights.

Your view is suddenly obscured as a flock of bats rises into the air ahead of you. But as you draw closer, you realise they aren't bats at all, but hideous winged imps – tiny airborne devils.

"What did I tell you?" calls La Befana over the wail of the wind in your ears. "The devil's agents are everywhere!"

And then the winged imps are upon you.

If you want to use *The Pen is Mightier* special ability, and you still can, cross off one use and turn to **6**. If you want to use the *Naughty or Nice* special ability, and you still can, turn to **478**. If you do not want to use either special ability, or you cannot, turn to **498**.

459

"If you've been naughty or if you've been nice,
With birch and with trap, I'll still strike you twice!"

And with that the Christmas Devil attacks! (In this battle you have the initiative.)

KRAMPUS	COMBAT 11	ENDURANCE 14

If Krampus wins a Combat Round, roll one die (or pick a card). If the number rolled is odd (or the card is red), he strikes you with his birch-whip (lose 2 *Endurance* points). If the number rolled is even (or the card is black), he catches you in the jaws of his man-trap (lose 2 *Endurance* points and reduce your *Combat* score by 1 point for the next Combat Round).

If you manage to win 3 Combat Rounds, or you reduce Krampus's *Endurance* score to 8 points or below, turn to **403** at once. If you do not manage either feat, the Christmas Devil will be victorious in this battle and your adventure will be over.

460

Roll one die (or pick a card). If the number rolled is odd (or the card is red), turn to **134**. If the number rolled is even (or the card is black), turn to **476**.

461

The corridor ends at a large wooden door bearing a grim visage carved into the wood – like some hideous cross between a man and a goat – while, on the lintel above the door, someone has painted the words, 'You'd Better Be Good for Goodness' Sake'.

Listening at the door for a moment, you hear what sounds like the muttering of low voices coming from behind it.

If you want to risk opening the door, turn to **441**. If you would rather leave well enough alone and want to follow the corridor the other way, turn to **362**.

462

Embossed onto the red leather cover of the huge tome in gold-leaf are three words: *Naughty or Nice*. The letters are clearly those that children from all over the world have sent to Father Christmas.

Do you want to take a closer look at the book (turn to **474**), or the letters (turn to **445**)?

463

The impish factory workers come for you then, armed with everything from mallets and ladles, to screwdrivers and even peppermint candy canes as big as shepherd's crooks!

If you want to use *The Pen is Mightier* special ability at this point, cross off one use and turn to **413**. If not, turn to **490**.

464

The blizzard bites deeper as you press on through the freezing night, clad in only your pyjamas, bed socks, slippers and a dressing-gown.

(Deduct 1 more *Endurance* point and 1 more *Agility* point.)

If you are still alive, turn to **484**.

465

You have done it! You have defeated the old man in the fur cloak! Before your very eyes, that is precisely what he becomes, now that the curse he was under has been lifted.

"Thank you," Venceslav whispers with his dying breath, and then is gone.

You will mourn the cursed king's passing, but another time; you have a mission to complete, and you will dedicate your victory, when it comes, to Venceslav the Accursed.

Leaving the dead man's body to be buried by the falling snow, you set off again, travelling north towards the dark teeth of the mountain range.

Turn to **244**.

466

Rather than trying to get away from you, the robin alights on a branch and waits for you to catch up before taking off again. Continuing in this way, it leads you to a hollow, within which stands the most curious cottage you have ever seen.

It looks like the sort of edible ornament you have out on the sideboard during the Christmas period, since it appears to be made entirely from gingerbread. From its sugar-work windows, to the piped icing decorating the windowsills and doorframe, the entire edifice appears to be edible. Even the snow dusting its roof looks like a sprinkling of icing sugar. But, curiously, there is smoke rising from its gingerbread chimney.

The robin hops about on the ground in front of the cottage chirruping frantically and flapping its wings furiously. But what is it trying to tell you?

Do you want to:

Taste a piece of gingerbread, to see if it is the real thing?	Turn to **426**.
Try the door?	Turn to **366**.
Leave the cottage and the clearing, and continue on your way?	Turn to **213**.

467

In spite of your best efforts, you lose sight of the cloaked figure fleeing through the fair. As you despondently start to make your way back between the market stalls to where you first entered this Dickensian scene, in the shadow of one of the bridge's arches, you see that someone has set up a Punch and Judy show. Standing beside the red-and-yellow-striped canvas booth is a little old man in a worn grey overcoat and wide-brimmed hat, with a thick white beard, and a red spotted kerchief tied about his neck.

The old man's dog, an Irish terrier, runs over to you and starts skipping around your feet.

Turn to **447**.

468

Gripping the box tightly with both hands, you prepare to push the brass button on its lid.

If you know what you need to do to go small, and you are sure you want to use the box, do it now. If you don't know, or you no longer want to use the box, turn to **489**.

469

You race away into the night, but running through deep snow in slippers, and with your dressing-gown flapping around your legs, is exhausting.

You are soon panting for breath and, your pace slowing, you hear the panting of the wolves behind you. Knowing that you can't outrun the hunters, you turn to face them instead.

Turn to **358**.

470

This sweet-toothed terror has tormented Mrs Christmas long enough. You always knew that too much sugar could be bad for you! (In this battle, the Candyman has the initiative.)

CANDYMAN	COMBAT 7	ENDURANCE 8

If you hack the spun-sugar psychopath to bits, turn to **430**.

471

"What do you think you're doing?" splutters the giantess, as she recovers her balance before she falls into the boiling cauldron. And then an evil grimace twists her already ugly features into an even more horrible sneer. "Try to boil me alive in my own cooking pot, would ya?"

Snatching up a cleaver the size of a woodcutter's axe, she turns on you.

"I'll butcher you like the dog you are!" she roars.

How will you respond to such threatening behaviour? Will you:

Use *The Pen is Mightier* special ability?	Turn to **96**.
Use your *Naughty or Nice* special ability?	Turn to **146**.
Prepare to defend yourself?	Turn to **116**.

472

You land in a snowdrift which breaks your fall, and you don't even sustain a scratch, although you are both cold and wet now.

Cross off one use of the *Naughty or Nice* special ability and turn to **422**.

473

The wind rises as the blizzard bites deeper.

If you have the code word *Kold* written down on your Adventure Sheet, turn to **493**. If not, turn to **244**.

474

The spine cracks as you open the ancient book, and you find yourself gazing upon column after column, and page after page, of names. Anywhere you look in the book, on the left-hand side are the names of those who have been deemed 'Naughty', written in black ink, while on the right-hand side, written in red ink, are the names of those whose deeds for the last year have classified them as 'Nice'.

Flicking through the huge ledger, gazing in wonder at the lists of names, you come to a double-page spread on which have been written only two names. On the left-hand page, in large black gothic letters is the name 'Krampus', while on the right-hand page, in red ink, is your name!

(You now have one extra use of the *Naughty or Nice* special ability; record this on your Adventure Sheet. If you want to take the book with you, add the Ledger of Souls to your list of Equipment and make a note that your name appears on page 400.)

You are suddenly aware of a fluttering sound, coming from the stone-built fireplace. It sounds like something has got stuck up the chimney. Will you:

Go over to the fireplace and take a look? Turn to **479**.

Read the letters written by children from all over the world? Turn to **389**.

Leave the office and continue your search for Father Christmas? Turn to **66**.

475

The present is large and when you try to lift it, you discover that it is heavy too. Your curiosity piqued, you skilfully rip off the wrapping paper and start to tug at the flaps of the box within.

Suddenly the present jerks out of your hands and lands on the floor with a thud. As you start to back away from it uneasily, the box twitches again and a sound like muffled laughter comes from inside.

In a movement so sudden it makes you jump, the box opens from within, and an articulated hand appears. It is followed by another, and then, in a flurry of feathers, the present's prisoner is free.

Standing on the floor in front of you is what appears to be a winged puppet. At first glance, it looks like a Christmas angel, or the fairy you might expect to see perched on top of the tree. Its wooden frame is covered by a tattered white dress and its oversized head is fashioned from china, which is cracked in places. Glass eyes roll in their sockets until they finally come to rest on you. The puppet's articulated jaws clacks open and it gives voice to a high-pitched giggle that is like the tinkling of a musical box.

Giggling insanely, the animated puppet reaches for you with twitching wooden fingers, its eyes rolling wildly inside its china head.

If you want to use *The Pen is Mightier* special ability now, cross off one use of the ability and turn to **373**. If you want to use the *Naughty or Nice* special ability, cross off one use and turn to **90**. If you do not want to use either of your special abilities yet, turn to **353**.

476

Just as you had hoped, the owner of the eye eventually loses interest and sinks back down to the lightless depths of the gelid lake.

Only when you are sure it has definitely gone do you start walking again, finally making it to the far shore of the lake and solid ground once more.

Turn to **446**.

477

The riddle reads as follows:

Ships on the Sea,
Fowls at the Feast,
Stars in the Sky.

If you are able to solve the riddle, you will end up with a three digit number; turn to the section with the same number now. However, if you are unable to answer the riddle, or the section you turn to makes no sense – meaning you have got it wrong – turn to **495**.

478

(Cross off one use of the *Naughty or Nice* special ability.)

As the imps come for you with fangs and claws bared, even more of the night-winged horrors rise from the shadowy forest, to ensure that you and the witch do not escape. (In this battle, the Winged Imps have the initiative.)

WINGED IMPS	COMBAT 8	ENDURANCE 12

If you reduce the imps' combined Endurance score to 4 points or fewer, turn to **6**.

If the imps win 3 consecutive Combat Rounds, one of the demons grabs you by the shoulders and pulls you off the back of the broomstick – turn to **26**.

479

If you have the code word *Kreepy* recorded on your Adventure Sheet, turn to **454**. If not, turn to **437.**

480

How do you intend to defend yourself against the Polar Bear?

If you are carrying the Mistletoe Spear, you will also have a number associated with the weapon. Divide this section number by the number linked to the spear, and then turn to this new section.

If you are not carrying the Mistletoe Spear, you will just have to do the best you can with whatever you do have – turn to **497**.

481

A piercing shriek cuts through the night – one of the whirling, rag-clad hags has spotted you!

You are soon surrounded, by wailing banshees as well as grotesquely-leering imps. The creatures of the devil's coven grasp you with their hideously clawed hands and drag you before the Lord of Misrule himself, gibbering and jabbering excitedly as they do so.

Krampus rises to his full impressive height before you and in a braying voice demands:

"Tell me, why are you here, you timorous mouse?
You've followed me ever since I left your house!"

Your heart racing, you stand tall and meet the monster's sinister caprine gaze. "I'm here to save Father Christmas!" you tell him.

"But why would you do that? What is he to you?
An agéd house-breaker whose time's overdue?"

"Because he brings joy to millions of children, all over the world. Because he reminds adults that it is better to give than to receive. And because, most importantly of all, in this instance it is not a case of 'better the devil you know'."

"Better the devil you know? You don't know me!
But you will soon enough, just you wait and see.
I've been around since mankind lived in caves,
When beasts ruled the night, and fear made them slaves.
Before there were saints, I was their master,
Causing their drums and their hearts to beat faster.
I was the monster, out there in the wood.
'Krampus will get you if you've not been good!'
That was a threat desperate mothers would make,
And, 'You'd better be good for goodness' sake!'
But then came the light, and then there came Christmas,
And I was banished – cast into the darkness!
Children slept soundly, all snug in their beds,
Sweet dreams, not nightmares, now filling their heads.
And they've become spoilt, and selfish, ungrateful,
Their manners appalling, their attitude hateful.
But I am the one who will punish the haughty,
And I will decide who is nice and who's naughty!
When I'm in charge, upon each Christmas Eve,
Sinners will tremble, for they will believe!
Children will wish for the old days. And hark!
People will know why they once feared the dark.
Christmas is dead! I have made it my pact;
From now on Christmas Eve will be called Krampusnacht!"

If you have at least one use of your *Naughty or Nice* special ability left, turn to **457** at once.

If not, turn to **369**.

482

The spine cracks as you open the ancient book, and you find yourself gazing upon column after column, and page after page, of names. Anywhere you look in the book, on the left-hand side are the names of those who have been deemed 'Naughty', written in black ink, while on the right-hand side, written in red ink, are the names of those whose deeds for the last year have classified them as 'Nice'.

Flicking through the huge ledger, gazing in wonder at the lists of names, you come to a double-page spread on which have been written only two names. On the left-hand page, in large black gothic letters is the name 'Krampus', while on the right-hand page, in red ink, is your name!

(You now have one extra use of the *Naughty or Nice* special ability; record this on your Adventure Sheet. If you want to take the book with you, add the Ledger of Souls to your list of Equipment and make a note that your name appears on page 400.)

Now turn to **479.**

483

The sight that greets you, when you reach the top of the hill, has you looking on in horror and disbelief.

A diabolical sigil has been marked out in the snow with soot, comprised of a pentagram bound within a circle. At each of the five points of the demonic star, there burns a brazier, fashioned from an upturned antlered skull atop a wooden pole.

But what is more horrible to your appalled gaze than the unholy symbol itself is the fact that a slightly overweight old man lies trussed up at its centre, and judging by his round belly, red coat and trousers, and white beard it can only be Father Christmas!

Standing at the bottom point of the inverted star is your nemesis, the one you have hunted for, far and wide this night, the hideous, horned, goat-leggéd Christmas Devil himself – Krampus!

Four crow-like figures, draped in tattered cloaks, stand behind the braziers that mark out the remaining four points of the pentagram, while more of the ragged figures whirl through the sky, black silhouettes against the coruscating Northern Lights.

The chanting voices of the figures drift to you over the snow, and although you cannot understand what they are saying, it nonetheless makes the hairs on the back of your neck stand on end.

You can only assume that the devil and his servants are enacting a dark rite to break Santa's power, doubtless intending to usurp his position. But whatever the truth of the matter, you know you have to do what you can to try to rescue Father Christmas from the foul fiend's clutches.

If you are in possession of the Box of Delights, there is a number you have associated with the magical item; turn to the section with the same number now.

If not, turn to **439**.

484

As you follow a path between two pine-clad ridges, the wind suddenly drops, and you see a wintry wonderland laid out before you, illuminated by the monochrome light of the now-visible moon.

The horizon is dominated by the jagged teeth of icy mountains, the tongue of a great glacier choking a pass between them. But before the mountains, to your right, lies a dark expanse of woodland, the brooding pines spreading almost as far as the black peaks, while to your left, at the other end of a valley that has been turned utterly white by the ever-present snow, you can see a frozen lake, and beyond that, rising from craggy foothills, an ice-clad castle.

Do you want to continue through the forest (turn to **496**), or make your way along the valley, towards the ice lake and frozen castle (turn to **256**)?

485

You are standing in what can only be described as a large office. The room is dominated by a huge stone fireplace, and there is a roaring fire burning within it even now. On one wall is a vast noticeboard, onto which have been pinned work schedules and a calendar-based planner on which the 24th December has been ringed in thick red pen. On the opposite wall is a huge map of the world.

Despite being larger than many people's homes, the office is crammed with filing cabinets and desks, and in one corner of the room is a veritable mountain of mail bags. Piles of opened letters cover the work stations.

Passing one of them, you see that it is covered with curled squares of yellowed parchment with things written on them like 'Jingle, don't forget to feed the reindeer', and 'Remind me to get something nice for Mrs Christmas'.

The largest desk – a monster of a thing that looks like it must have been put together from an entire oak tree – stands in front of the fire, and clearly belongs to the boss. There are stacks of open envelopes on this desk too, as well as a large, leather-bound book.

However, the office is entirely devoid of human life, or any other form of life for that matter.

As well as the double doors leading to the factory floor, there is another, smaller way in and out facing the fireplace.

You can't help feeling that time is running out so do you want to leave the office through the smaller door without further delay (turn to **66**), or do you want to examine the things on Father Christmas's desk first (turn to **462**)?

486

You race away into the night but, running through deep snow in slippers and with your dressing-gown flapping around your legs, you don't have a chance of outrunning the wolves.

One of the animals launches itself at you, pulling you to the ground and sinking its fangs into your shoulder. (Deduct 2 *Endurance* points.)

Kicking the animal off you, you scramble to your feet and prepare to fight for your life.

Turn to **358**.

487

You set off at a stilted run after the fleeing figure, artfully dodging the other people attending the fair, ducking between market stalls, and twisting around pirouetting skaters, as you try to keep the figure in sight.

You get the impression of a ragged, fur-lined cloak, coloured a deep crimson, and it looks like the figure has a wicker basket strapped to its back.

Take an Agility test; if you pass the test, turn to **387**, but if you fail the test, turn to **467**.

488

The Candyman stalks towards you on lollipop legs and feet of fudge. Will you:

Use *The Pen is Mightier* special ability if you can?	Turn to **450**.
Attack the creepy confection?	Turn to **470**.
Call his name three times, in the hope of banishing him?	Turn to **16**.

489

Taking a firm grip on the Ice Sword, you prepare to defend yourself from the Snowmen's icicle claws and teeth with the frozen blade. (In this battle, the Snowmen have the initiative, but you can fight them one at a time. However, if you have the code word *Kursed* recorded on your Adventure Sheet, you must reduce your *Combat* score by 2 points for the duration of this battle.)

	COMBAT	ENDURANCE
First SNOWMAN	6	7
Second SNOWMAN	7	7

If you manage to put an end to both of the abominable Snowmen, turn to **408**.

490

As the warped workers bear down on you, you have no choice but to fight the nearest four all together! (In this battle, the Imps have the initiative.)

	COMBAT	ENDURANCE
First IMP	7	6
Second IMP	6	7
Third IMP	6	6
Fourth IMP	7	7

If you vanquish all of the Imps, you begin to despair as, unperturbed, another four step forward to take their place – turn to **413**.

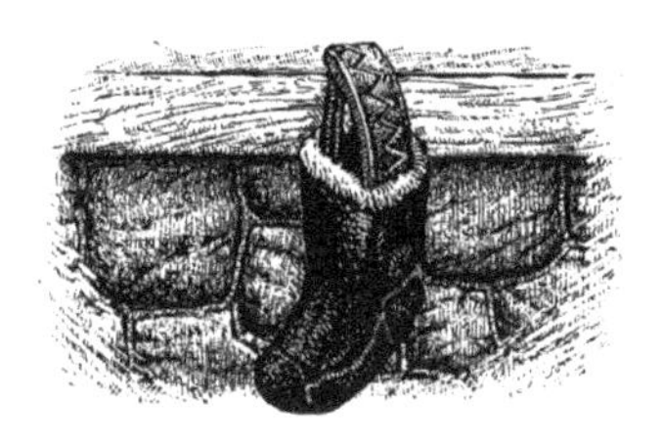

491

With an almighty splash, the giantess topples into the boiling cauldron.

Record the code word *Kretinous* on your Adventure Sheet and turn to **199**.

492

You find yourself in a broad corridor, lit with holly-wreathed Christmas lanterns, that runs both left and right. Echoing from the right you can hear a noisy clattering, while to the left you can hear nothing at all. So which way do you want to go?

Left?	Turn to **461**.
Right?	Turn to **362**.

493

The rapidly dropping temperature takes its toll on your already cold and weary body.

(Deduct 2 *Endurance* points, 1 *Agility* point, and 1 *Combat* point.)

If you are still alive, now turn to **244**.

494

Can this night get any stranger? (It is the Gingerbread Men who have the initiative in this battle, and you have to fight them all at the same time.)

	COMBAT	ENDURANCE
First GINGERBREAD MAN	7	2
Second GINGERBREAD MAN	6	2
Third GINGERBREAD MAN	5	2
Fourth GINGERBREAD MAN	6	2
Fifth GINGERBREAD MAN	7	2
Sixth GINGERBREAD MAN	6	2

If you win the fight, turn to **32**.

495

Frustratingly, you do not know the number to which the stone tumblers need to be set, and so you cannot hope to claim to the white-wood spear – whatever it is.

Perhaps you could force the chamber's evergreen guardians to reveal the number to you. If you want to try this heavy-handed approach, turn to **417**. Otherwise, you have no choice but to descend the creepers and return to the courtyard – turn to **381**.

496

The trees envelope you in pine-scented darkness. The moon disappears from sight, hidden by the snow-clad branches, and soon you have no idea which way you are heading through the forest. You could be going round in circles for all you know.

And then you enter a moonlit clearing and spy a red-breasted robin hopping about in the snow. It twitters at you and then takes off, disappearing between the evergreens.

If you want to try to follow the robin, turn to **466**. If you would rather trust to your own instincts and struggle on alone, turn to **213**.

497

You are petrified, facing down an adult male Polar Bear, but if you don't find some previously untapped reserve of courage deep within to draw on, you are going to be slaughtered by the beast, out here on the snowy hillside. (In this battle, the Polar Bear has the initiative.)

POLAR BEAR	COMBAT 10	ENDURANCE 13

If you somehow manage to win your fight with the beast, turn to **465**.

498

The night-winged horrors are a black cloud against the velvet blue of the star-pricked sky.

You are forced to fend them off while La Befana struggles to maintain control of the broomstick. (In this battle, the Winged Imps have the initiative.)

WINGED IMPS	COMBAT 7	ENDURANCE 8

If you reduce the imps' combined *Endurance* score to 4 points or fewer, turn to **6**.

If the imps win 3 consecutive Combat Rounds, one of the demons grabs you by the shoulders and pulls you off the back of the broomstick – turn to **26**.

499

As you thrust the bloodied tip of the spear into the animal's flesh for a third time, the polar bear gives a great roar and rises up on its hind-legs, as if it is about to drop its full weight on top of you and end you. But rather than kill you, the bear starts to change again.

The beast shrinks in stature, its great claws retracting into its body, and its muzzle flattening to become a face again, until cursed King Venceslav stands before you once more, clad in a white bearskin cloak.

"Thank you! Thank you!" he cries, tears streaming down his cheeks. "I have been under a curse all these years, but this night, thanks to your courage and the power of the Mistletoe Spear, the enchantment has been lifted and I am free to live my life once more. Bless you!"

Gain one additional use of both *The Pen is Mightier* and the *Naughty or Nice* special abilities, for freeing Venceslav from the bear-curse.

The huskies have not gone far, and soon the two of you are back in the sled. Venceslav carries you north, to the very edge of the mountains, and then departs, heading towards the south and his future, whatever that may hold for him now.

Turn to **244**.

500

The anti-Santa defeated, his coven banished, and Father Christmas safe once more, the saint thanks you for coming to his rescue.

"What will you do now?" you ask him. "Krampus and his cronies have ruined everything."

"It's nothing that can't be repaired or rebuilt," Father Christmas assures you, his ancient eyes twinkling.

"But what about this Christmas?"

"What about it?" he asks.

"There isn't enough time left for you to finish delivering your presents."

"For Father Christmas, there's always just enough time. But I agree, we have to hurry."

"We?" you gasp, flabbergasted.

"You weren't planning on walking home, were you?" chuckles the Big Man.

Returning to his workshop, Santa tethers his reindeer to his sleigh once more, and you join him in the driver's seat.

"Now, Dasher! Now, Dancer! Now, Prancer and Vixen! On, Comet! On, Cupid! On, Donner and Blitzen!" he shouts as he pulls on the reins. "Now dash away! Dash away! Dash away all!"

More rapid than eagles, his coursers take to the air, pulling the sleigh after them and leaving the arctic wilderness far behind in the blink of an eye.

As you soar through the sky faster than a rocket, you peer over the side and through gaps in the clouds hurtling past below you, you catch glimpses of seas, fields, forests and towns, until suddenly you are descending again, and, at their master's command, the reindeer alight outside your house.

In a daze, your mind awhirl, you climb down onto the snowy ground in front of your own front door.

Father Christmas gives you a smile and a wink. "I'll be seeing you again, my friend," he says, laying a finger aside his nose.

He gives a shrill whistle, the reindeer take off in a flurry of snow, and away they fly once more, as if they were all as weightless as thistledown.

You watch them go as, from inside the house, you hear the grandfather clock in the hall chime one. For a moment you see the sleigh silhouetted against the glowing orb of the moon, before it vanishes from sight altogether, and the echo of a booming shout reaches your ears.

"Happy Christmas to all, and to all a goodnight!"

The End

Acknowledgements

There are a number of people without whose help this festive frolic of a book would not have become what it is, so here and now would seem like the perfect place to thank them.

First of all, my grateful thanks go to the illustrator, Tony Hough. Tony and I first worked together twenty-five years ago, when we were both a lot less grey than we are now, after Puffin Books commissioned him to produce the illustrations for my second Fighting Fantasy gamebook, the now very hard to get hold of *Knights of Doom,* and we collaborated again twelve years later, on the book *Bloodbones.* Over the years, Tony's style has changed and developed, but he still does dark very well, and his illustrations contain the most wonderful details, a combination that made him the ideal artist to realise the world of *'TWAS – The Krampus Night Before Christmas.*

Secondly, thank you to Emma Barnes at Snowbooks for her encouragement and support, and thirdly, to Anna Torborg, for doing such a fantastic job on the layout, and helping to turn out such a fabulous-looking book.

I must also thank those people who helped create the various Kickstarter rewards, namely Kevin Abbotts, for the bookmarks and the hyperlinked eBook version of the adventure, and Fil Baldowski of All Rolled Up for producing the Krampus-themed dice trays and game rolls.

But it would be most remiss of me if I failed to offer a huge and heartfelt thank you to everyone who pledged their support to this quirky venture from the outset, and joined me on my journey to the North Pole. Without them, this book would not exist. And so I toast you now, by raising the wassail bowl, and with the words of this old English saying:

"So we keep the olden greeting
With its meaning deep and true,
And wish you a merrie Christmas
And a happy New Year to you."

Kickstarter Backers

Santa's Little Helpers

Adriano Ziffer

Candy Canes

Jason Shepherd • Darren Buckley

Electronic Elves

Mark Crew • Sapper Joe • Kenny Beecher • Kino • David Wolf • Emma Gelgoot • Zoran Blackie • Adam Sparshott • Jonny Fontana • Stephen Leck • Matthias Ludonauter darkpact Nagy • Sam Wright • Claudia • Clan Bowers • Christopher Semler

Rogue Reindeer

Michael Hartley • Mark Stoneham • Niki Lybæk • Andrew Hartley • Andrew Alvis • Bernadine Phillips • Amanda Jeffries • Chris Jefferson • Stéphane Bechard • Tim Wild • Rob Crewe • Simone Carlini • Joe Tilbrook • Steve Lord • Jules Fattorini • Michael Reilly • Dave Bowen • Gonçalo Rodrigues • Natsutan • Hans Peter Bak • Retro Roleplayer • Michael Knarr • Zack Ronan McGinnis • Kim Morrison • Shelly Leonard • Alistair Davidse • Pikey Berbil • Jesse Raymond Ames • Nicodemus • Gwendlyn Drayton • Dane Barrett • Stuart Lloyd • Luke Paul Sanders • Jeffrey Dean • Luca Skorpio • Israel Cordero • Zacharias Chun-Pong Leung 梁振邦 • Jim Manchester • Olivier Leclair • Jay V Schindler • The LeDés • Pang Peow Yeong & family • Olly Mc • Derrick Bergeron • Kjeld Froberg • Peter BB • Stephen Redmond • Rob Hodgson • James Price • Della-Ann Sewell • Tom Cottrell • Leah Zinn • Jessica Rose • Dustin Beard • Sarinee Achavanuntakul • Cheryl Sirois • Russel Dalenberg • Catt McLeod • Charles Lonborg • Ron Weekes • Niall Holden • Thomas Henry Rove Fielding • Sarah Henderson • Evie + Alex McKenzie • Jamie Fry • Narciso (nj) Jaramillo • Amanda Bennett • Simon Day • Ian Fincham • Steve Yost • Luke Sheridan • The Crounk Family • Russell Owen • A Donaghey • Robert Wilde • Jim Miles • Sarah Corpé • Jay Capodiferro • Richie Stevens • Shawn Lowman • Jonathan Adams • Paul Taylor •Simon Hedley • Matt Sheriff • Kevin S. • Chris Basler • Gaetano Abbondanza • Jonas Sværke • Paul Gresty • Andrew Gaskell • Scott H. Moore • Timothy Haritun • Ciak • James Pierce • Paul Gaston • Pete Wood • Antonio Moxedano • Doc Hogan • Clay Skaggs • Gilles Manasselian • Gareth and Dylan Morgan • Ludvig • Mark Lee Voss • Lisa Sustaita • N. Tanksley • Gabrielle Meester • Ian & Lucy MacLellan • Ken Nagasako • Ed Kiernan • Stephen Haunts

• Matt Leitzen • Richard Bunting • Melanie Calion Mendoza • Jake Riffe • Louisa Oaten • Prof. Dr. Oliver M. Traxel • Kieran Coghlan • VERNET Laurent • Ashley Hall • Kevin Harvey • Duncan, Blaine, and Jason Lenox • Ols Jonas Petter Olsson • Gabor Geza Kiss • Adrian Jankowiak • Luis Lauranzon III • John Mazzeo • Cheryl Marie Sirois • Scott Kuhn • KT Savacool • Aaron Coy Goodson

Christmas Crackers

Peter 'Malkira' Lennox • Graham Hart • Marc Thorpe • Chris Trapp • Y. K. Lee • Phil Riches • Andy Bow • Ang NamLeng • Dominic Marcotte • Keith Woodson • Caelin, Nate, and Rowan Johnson • Tjalle Klijnstra • Anders Svensson • Keith Tollfree • Phillip Bailey • Ant O'Reilly • Ian Greenfield • Erica M Ruyle • Federico Catalano • Robert Wheeler • Vin de Silva • Andrew Shannon • Mario Villanueva • Hobocufflinks • Ryan D. Aldous Hutchins • Brian V. O'Keefe • Splunkjamma • Emerson Kasak • Andrew Wright • Greg Bouin • James Aukett • Andy "VaultsOfExtoth" Wears • Matt Taylor • Brian Waterhouse • Robin Mayenfels • Geoffrey Bertram • Brad Anderson • Magnus Johansson • Maggie Kulzer • Xavier/Miriam/Leia Aixendri Moneny • Pat Breen • Anthony Christopher Hackett

Stuffed Stockings

林立人 Lin Liren • René Batsford • Jessica Taylor-Abbotts • Colin Deady • Colin Oaten • Harvey Howell • DK • Simon J. Painter • Stephanie M. • Javier Fernández-Sanguino • Sauro Lepri • Simon Scott • Allan Matthews • Arthur Lewis Settle • Judykins • Kristen Patton-Schulle • Betsy J • Timithy Klesick • Naked Genius • Rob Lord • Bryan K. Borgman • Drew Smith • Rms • Jonathan Caines • Rhel • Ondřej Zástěra • Alexander Ballingall • Naab

Secret Santas

Tansy Catherine Susan Hirons • Jason Vince a.k.a. Dreamwalker Spirit • Sterling R. Scherff • Vitas Varnas • Steve Pitson • Fabrice Gatille • Crystal McCarty • Paul, Noah, Jona & Elya Brückner • David Poppel • Cande y Vic • Pat O'Neill

'TWAS Christmas Cards

Erin Cavanaugh

'TWAS Playing Cards and Dice

Des B

'TWAS ARU Game Roll

John Dennis

About the Author

Jonathan Green is a writer of speculative fiction, with more than seventy books to his name. Well known for his contributions to the Fighting Fantasy range of adventure gamebooks, he has also written fiction for such diverse properties as *Doctor Who, Star Wars: The Clone Wars, Warhammer, Warhammer 40,000, Sonic the Hedgehog, Teenage Mutant Ninja Turtles, Moshi Monsters, LEGO, Judge Dredd, Robin of Sherwood,* and *Frostgrave*.

He is the creator of the *Pax Britannia* series for Abaddon Books and has written eight novels, and numerous short stories, set within this steampunk universe, featuring the debonair dandy adventurer Ulysses Quicksilver. He is also the author of an increasing number of non-fiction titles, including the award-winning *YOU ARE THE HERO – A History of Fighting Fantasy Gamebooks* series.

He occasionally edits and compiles short story anthologies, such as the critically-acclaimed *GAME OVER, SHARKPUNK,* and *Shakespeare Vs Cthulhu*, all of which are published by Snowbooks.

To find out more about ACE Gamebooks and his other projects, visit www.JonathanGreenAuthor.com and follow him on Twitter @jonathangreen

Lightning Source UK Ltd.
Milton Keynes UK
UKHW012344201119
353920UK00003B/135/P